DANCING WITH DYSPRAXIA

First published in 2008 by

WOODFIELD PUBLISHING LTD
Bognor Regis ~ West Sussex ~ England ~ PO21 5EL
www.woodfieldpublishing.com

The right of Hazel Carr
to be identified as Author of this work
has been asserted in accordance with
the Copyright, Designs and Patents Act 1988

ISBN 1-84683-052-4

Dancing with Dyspraxia

*A Practical Guide for
Parents & Teachers*

HAZEL CARR

Woodfield

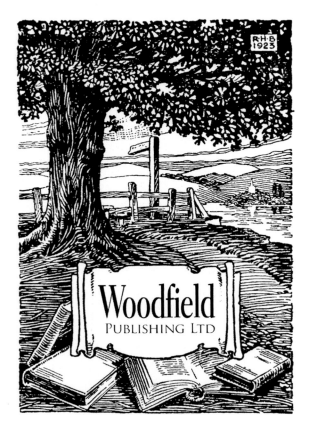

Woodfield Publishing Ltd

Woodfield House ~ Babsham Lane ~ Bognor Regis ~ West Sussex ~ PO21 5EL
telephone 01243 821234 ~ **e-mail** enquiries@woodfieldpublishing.co.uk

Interesting and informative books on a variety of subjects

For full details of all our published titles, visit our website at
www.woodfieldpublishing.co.uk

Dedicated to my sister Susan,
who is the bravest of them all.

To Bernard, my "guardian angel",
who taught me to care for others,

Those "others" are now caring for me.

~ CONTENTS ~

Acknowledgements

I was not born to be brave, have tolerance and compassion, to be caring, loving and happy ~ I was given opportunities in life by these people…

With many thanks to my family: Elliot, Sophie and Maisy, the Whites, Trysciaks, Newells and Carrs, for loving me, whatever.

Heather and Michelle, who tolerate me every day with a smile.

Peter Forde and Dr Tiny Aroura who were my inspiration.

To the lady who worked so hard in editing this book and didn't want to change the "essence of the story" ~ as she said ~ but didn't want to be mentioned.

To Dr John Rack, who believed in me and shared my story.

To Helen Bray Studios, Nigel and Harry for their beautiful cover.

All the staff at Holmfirth J. I. & N School, who have all been part of changing and improving many lives over the years, as well as mine.

A special thank you to all the children and parents who are part of this story.

Special moments take seconds, but last a lifetime.

The children I work with take years…

But it's worth waiting for.

Introduction

I started working in a mainstream school many years ago as a volunteer, to support my son, who had been diagnosed with severe dyslexia. He was very articulate and was average at reading and spelling, but his handwriting was the problem. He had difficulty forming letters and writing sentences took hours. But, as the old saying goes, "practice makes perfect" and I went along with it by making him practice.

Looking back now, he never did get perfect, but worse...

I also went along with the diagnosis, by experts, as I was young, ignorant and taught by my parents to respect authority. In their defence, little was known, then, about dyspraxia.

It wasn't until over five years ago, when I attended a course as a learning support assistant for the same school, that I realised my mistakes.

As a LSA I supported many children over the years with Autism, Asperger's, ADHD, cerebral palsy, dyslexia and other learning and behaviour difficulties.

Many years ago, when I started as a LSA, our main purpose in school was general support for children in class: photocopying, laminating, etc. Now schools recognise the importance of LSAs as experts in special needs.

Working with special needs children over the years I realised that they all had similar degrees of difficulties of high motor activity, slow at processing (not following instructions) gross/fine motor skills, balance, direction, judgement of distance, right/left laterality and learning/ behaviour difficulties.

This programme is not only for children diagnosed with dyspraxia, it is for all children who have motor skills difficulties (whatever the degree of weakness).

Children are unable to reach their full potential in school and, through experience, I know that many children are investigated for other difficulties when the root cause is motor skills.

Many children are given the label of having dyspraxia when every resource in school has been exhausted and parents need an answer. Children may be given the label but, unfortunately, funding for dyspraxia is seen as the lowest priority for support and many parents are left to their own resources.

Failure in school inevitably resulted in the lowest self-esteem children should have to experience.

With the support of my school, I started an exercise programme over five years ago.

I read many books over the years, but none of them told you about the emotions, frustrations and the pitfalls along the way. What I wasn't expecting, was the change in the children as they overcame their difficulties.

Children without motor skills difficulties now ask to join the programme because they can see how much fun we have and we are now a special club.

But many children have to go home every day and do exercises from a booklet on their own. This is fine if you have no alternative, but as a team you start *belonging*.

The most important effect of all was that over 80 children's self-esteem increased to superhuman levels as they witnessed their own success every day ~ and these children no longer struggled.

The programme I deliver every day is part of our school and it is fully supported. The importance of difficulties with motor skills is recognised and our children are now making progress.

Staff recognise symptoms themselves in class and, together as a whole school, we support these children with special needs. And when I say 'staff' I mean everyone from the cook to the caretakers. We all are aware of the children and their difficulties and from the minute they enter school their welfare is as important as any of the children.

I see this programme as a Mercedes car (a child with motor skills difficulties) with all the luxuries you can imagine (quality teaching), but it still won't go. The car goes at last because the only thing missing is the petrol (the Programme). They both needed that missing piece to kick-start them.

This book is not full of graphs, percentages and long words that you won't understand. I wrote it for ordinary parents, like myself, who need help.

The children I have supported on this programme are now a statistic, but for *achievement* not failure.

What Are Motor Skills Difficulties?

When I first read about dyspraxia, this was the kind of explanation I read:

"Sensory integrative dysfunction"

"Ideational dyspraxia and ideamotor dyspraxia"

It is really clever how many long words they have used but, guess what? I hadn't got a clue what they meant! It is fine if you're trained in this field. Many doctors who are asked for advice and guidance from worried parents usually refer the child to another agency such as an Occupational Therapist. This is why I hope I can explain motor skills difficulties in a way you will understand.

To me, if your child has been labelled as having dyspraxia, this is when every resource has been exhausted and children's difficulties are becoming embedded. As every child is an individual, so is the severity and quantity of symptoms. This is how I simplify and explain motor skills difficulties or, for short, MSD. I now catch children *before* they start to have problems.

Research says that if a baby is lying in a cot and you are dangling a toy above it, the baby will kick and reach out, moving its arms and legs trying to grasp it. The messages that are supposed to go to its arm and hand are going to all four limbs, except where it's supposed to go. This is because messages are going along unnecessary neural pathways.

If you could look inside your baby's brain you would see millions of neural pathways, or as one child said, "It's like spaghetti in your head all mixed up and the exercises will unravel it".

By the time it is six months old a baby is almost "reflexively" able to hold a dangling toy. As a child repeatedly uses the same neural pathways they will then transmit messages between five nerve junctions. At six months this is reduced to three and this movement becomes a "rapid response".

There are five operations (or paths) in a younger child compared to three in the older child. Not only is the speed of information increased but it is much less likely that information will be misdirected. Unfortunately, with a child with MSD the unnecessary neural pathways do not disappear. This is when you are able to understand the delayed processing and associated movements, which become a problem in children.

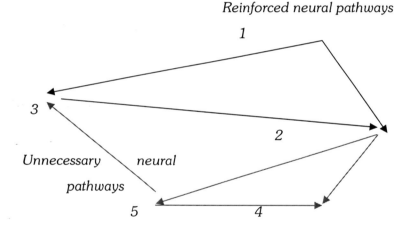

To a teacher or parent without knowledge of MSD a child can appear "naughty, careless or not following instructions" as messages go around and around.

Imagine a teacher talking to a class of children; by the fifth sentence a child with MSD is still processing the first.

A child with MSD/dyspraxia is unable to move with a rapid response and when you screen children for MSD you will see that when a child is required to move one limb, all limbs move (associated movements). You can screen children by watching them in PE or even the playground as they may run and flap with their arms and hands.

The most effective screening method is in Madeleine Portwood's Book "Developmental Dyspraxia". If you ask a child to walk on his/her tiptoes forwards and then walk backwards without turning around, the child's hands will go down. When walking on heels, the hands will go up. A child will be asked to walk with feet turned in and then walking with feet out; again the hands will turn in or out.

A child will be asked to touch each finger to its thumb; this not only tests for processing information to the fingers but the co-ordination for movement of fine motor skills.

You also look for the other hand to see if it mirrors the movements.

A sheet of paper is put over a child's wrist and they look away; you stroke two fingers and they have to tell which fingers were stroked. MSD children have difficulty in telling which fingers.

I use a beanbag and ask a child to throw it from one hand to the next: this is to see if a child tracks the beanbag with his/her eyes. They may throw the bag onto his/her chest (unable to cross their mid line) and they are also unable to grasp the beanbag with strength.

There are more tests to screen children for MSD, but by observing children continually (and reading this book) and gaining knowledge of MSD, difficulties become obvious in a school/home environment.

An Educational Response

The brain is up made of two parts. The left hemisphere separates out parts which make a whole; the right combines the parts to create a whole. You need access to both sides to enable them to work together.

As well as having difficulty with processing, children I have supported were unable to progress past the CVC (consonant-vowel-consonant stage). Because of weakness in one side of the brain/body (as I saw it) they struggled with phonics, which is introduced in Nursery and Reception. Once the weakness in their body was corrected this problem ceased in that they were able to progress in phonics past the CVC stage.

All the children I worked with on the programme showed a prominent weak side when exercising. One of the first movements that a child needs to master, to stimulate the left and right hemisphere, is crawling. When screening and exercising I introduce crawling. I have seen children (up to 11 years old) unable to co-ordinate their left and right, they lift their whole body up into a crab position and gallop.

Left Hemisphere	*Right Hemisphere*
B	Broken
r k o	
n e	

Over the years as a support assistant you go on many courses and notice how many children have very similar symptoms. These are what experts call "associated behaviours".

The cortex in the brain controls the sensory systems (touch, smell, taste, etc) its motor responses (movement) and the behaviours of thought and language (thinking and speaking). The cortex surrounds the limbic system, which controls the "instinctive" part of the brain that controls the automatic responses in the body. It is also involved in emotional behaviour.

In a child without any difficulties, the cortex "dampens" the effect of the limbic system. Because of the MSD the cortex has many millions of weak neural pathways and cannot "dampen" the limbic system, which holds these unwanted behaviours. It's like having a weak flood wall and the water comes flooding in with all the debris. This is why many children are investigated for other associated behaviours from the limbic system, when the root cause is dyspraxia.

Children could be investigated for ADHD because they showed signs of high motor activity. Children on the programme whose balance was "unbalanced" showed up as a weak side when exercising. Children would move around, as one child once said, "to stop me feeling dizzy." Again, similar symptoms but dyspraxia was the root cause. This is why it is very difficult sometimes to obtain a specific diagnosis and other conditions (ADHD, autism/Asperger's and dyslexia) are also diagnosed and children are put in this spectrum. Once children had been on the Programme and neural pathways had been strengthened, many of these associated movements/ behaviours either disappeared or behaviour could be managed and changed.

I have simplified, very briefly, dyspraxia although there are many books which will give you pages of research and use the correct medical terms.

I was interested in the exercises in books as this supported me in my quest to find the best solution to produce the best programme. But when it came to putting theory into practice, I was on my own.

I hope by reading about my experiences this book will give you the motivation and inspire you to start your own programme and make a difference to a lot of lives.

1. Jack

Jack is six years old, nearly seven, although he can't always remember. He isn't very big for his age and his Mum is always saying to everyone "Our Jack will never put weight on because he never stops, he's like a flea is our Jack."

Jack lives with his Mum and Dad in a lovely big house next to Mrs Roberts. He likes Mrs Roberts because she talks to him about when she was little and worked in the mill. They talk for hours about all sorts of things, she's like his Nan.

Jack hasn't got any brothers or sisters although he heard his Mum telling Mrs Roberts next door that she would like another. Instead he will have to manage with his pet gerbil, Stan, for now.

Jack can hear in his sleepy haze his Mum shouting for him to get up, but he's all warm and snuggly in bed. He was having a lovely dream. She's woken him up now. Never mind, he can't remember what his dream was about anyway.

His Mum bursts in to the bedroom Whoosh!

"**Jack** will you get up! I've been shouting you for ages, look at this bedroom it's a pigsty. **Jack** get out of bed we're going to be late, as always, and don't think that I'm dressing you because you're not a baby. Come on **Jack. Jack,** come on, it's school!"

Suddenly Jack realises that it's Monday and it's school. He hates school, he feels sick now. Then he remembers all the work he's downloaded from the computer on dinosaurs for the topic they are doing and he hopes Mrs Mack, his teacher, will be impressed because he rarely makes her smile.

He jumps out of bed but falls because he can't remember leaving that mess on the floor. Oh! flip, his leg is wrapped around the duvet.

"**Jack,** what are you doing? Will you stop messing about and hurry up, we're going to be late."

Jack picks up the papers that are on the floor: he must have left them there last night. He's got loads on dinosaurs for school. He'll just read the bit about T-Rex because he hasn't read that bit, that bit is really interesting.

"**Jack!** Are you ready, have you had a wee?"

Whoops! Jack forgot about school and getting ready.

Jack goes into the bathroom and has a wee. His mum always reminds him to go to the toilet as he sometimes has accidents at school. His bum needs him to go but by the time he gets the messages to his brain, it's too late. That really makes Mrs Smith mad. She is always saying, "Why didn't you tell me in time Jack?"

Jack's classmates call him "Piddly-Pants" and tease him, but he hasn't told his Mum.

He tries to go lots of times, just in case, but they have a rule in class which means they have to go at break time so that they don't lose valuable teaching time.

He goes into the bathroom and fills the sink up with water. He gives his face a quick wipe with the face cloth but the water goes all over his jim-jams because he never seems to squeeze all the water out.

He never gets his toothpaste on his brush. If he puts the tube onto the sink and presses it, sometimes it squeezes out, other times it goes all over. He can't get his hand right to brush his teeth, it's easier to move his head and keep his brush still because his hands sometimes feel really wobbly and he can't grip things properly, but that makes him go dizzy.

"Jack."

Now then, what was he doing?

"**Jack!** Are you dressed?"

Oh, flip flip flip! That was it, he has to put his clothes on. Never mind, he'll play with his plastic boats another time.

Jack goes in his bedroom and starts to get his clothes out of his drawers. He hates this, he knows he has to put his socks on first but he never gets them on right. He can't get his thumbs in like his Mum showed him and then pull them over his toes as they always end up inside out and upside down. Jack lies on his back and puts his feet up and pulls his undies on. He's tried standing up but he can't balance and he falls over. He does the same with his trousers but he can't get his zip up or fasten the button as his fingers don't do what he wants them to. His Mum is always saying, "Oh Jack! You're all fingers and thumbs," in fact all old people say things like that.

That's why he never likes games like marbles and Lego because he can never pick up little fiddly things. His Nana always buys him them on Birthdays or at Christmas because she's always saying, "He'll get the hang of it one day, he's a boy, boys need to build."

He puts his T-shirt on but gets his head stuck and then he loses his balance and feels dizzy because he can't see. OHHHHH! BUMP!

He can hear his Mum talking even though he can't see her.

"**Jack!** Are you messing about again? Oh look! Get up you silly boy! Your socks aren't on properly, you haven't fastened your trousers and your T-shirt is inside out. Every day I end up dressing you, you're like a baby, you're nearly seven you know, for goodness sake."

Jack's Mum pushes and pulls him into his clothes and then points him towards the door with a very angry look, muttering about how nothing he wears matches.

"I'm a boy Mum, not a fashion icon." He remembered that from watching Trinny and Susanna on telly. Jack thinks this to himself but doesn't think he should mention it as his Mum is a bit mad now.

Jack goes downstairs and into the kitchen and tries to sit on the chair but falls off. His Mum lifts him off the floor and starts counting, he doesn't know why at her age she can only count to ten, she's always doing that lately.

She puts a bowl in front of Jack and while she isn't looking he puts his hand in the box of cereal and gets a handful out. If his Mum saw him do that she would go mad, but if he poured them from the box and spilt them like he always does she would be even madder.

Jack has his cereal dry because it's easier and not as messy, but his crispies still fly all over because he can't quite hold his spoon without it wobbling.

He likes to eat the same thing anyway because he doesn't like to try something new.

"Come on Jack we have to go," shouts his Mum. "Put your shoes on."

He tries to put his shoes on but he can never do the laces, he always remembers the left foot because Mrs Clarke at school taught him to make an L with his left hand to remind him which was his left. He waddles out to the car with his shoes falling half on and off.

He climbs into the car and his Mum asks if he has his seat belt on.

"Yes Mum."

He hasn't really because it's too hard; he just holds it so it looks like he has. His Mum asks him if he's got everything, and he checks, but it doesn't make any difference because he always forgets something. He likes it on the way to school because his Mum chats to him and he has time to listen to her and nothing distracts him.

They arrive at school and his Mum puts her arms around him and gives him a kiss. She wipes her sleeve across his face and straightens his hair. She tucks him in and bends down to tie his shoes.

"Every morning I tie your shoes Jack! You're a big boy now Jack! Big boys should be able to tie shoes by now."

"Mum, all the others in my class have Velcro, can't I have Velcro?"

Jack looks up at his Mum, like his Nana's dog when it begs.

"Well you're not lazy like those babies. They never had Velcro when I was a little girl, now be a big boy." MMMMA! She gives him a warm snuggly kiss and pushes him into the playground.

Jack walks along the wall and rests against the classroom window: he hates the playground, it is so noisy. He never runs around if he can help it because he knows he will be knocked over or trip over or bump into someone. His Mum is shouting and waving goodbye to him, he can't wait for home time. Most days he cries and has tummy ache and every day he tells his Mum he hates her because she is the one making him go to school.

He gets angry and he sometimes hits her. He can hit her because she loves him and she always will love him whatever he does to her. But she still sends him, he hates school.

Mrs Mack, his class teacher, comes out and shouts something, but there is so much noise. He gets pulled and pushed and he follows everyone as it looks as though they are lining up. He's learnt to follow the other children when they move because he can't always hear. The trouble is, he sometimes copies naughty George and then Mrs Mack says, "If George jumped off a cliff, would you Jack?" and then he's in trouble. That's another old people thing she says, and anyway, he would use a parachute, he's not stupid. She wouldn't believe him when he said he didn't let the fire extinguisher off; it was George who told him to. Mrs Mack shouts again but he can't hear because the other children are all talking, so he waits until they are all in the cloakroom.

"Jack! I might have known you would be last! Come on!" grumbles Mrs Smith. Mrs Smith is the teaching assistant who works in his class. She's always watching him with her little beady eyes ~ not that he would say that to her.

Jack walks in to a mass of bodies moving about in the corridor and they are all pushing and pulling. He waits until they have all gone into class, but how on earth is he supposed to see where his peg is now? His peg used to have his name on it but the name dropped off and he gets mixed up with Josh and Jessie because that's a J for jigsaw. In Nursery it was brilliant because he was a lemon. Was it in the middle or to the left or right? He can never remember.

He tries to get his coat off but can't, he's learnt that if you use the hook on the wall you can hook the collar at the back and ease it off. It looks odd but it works.

Mrs Smith the TA pokes her head out of the classroom and looks at Jack.

"He's here Mrs Mack, he's messing around as usual, come on Jack its register." She's standing at the door with her arms folded across her big chest ~ not that he would say that she had a big chest ~ his Nana has a big chest.

Jack decides to just put his bag down and go into class but he trips because he's got his bag strap around his legs, he'd forgotten about the straps.

"I might have known you would do that Jack, go and sit down over there," says Mrs Smith.

Jack knows he is going to have to manoeuvre across the carpet to the space and he knows he is going to fall. The children are all looking at him because they know he will.

He steadies himself by holding the children's heads and wobbling from side to side. The children grumble as he goes past and he eventually falls on Tom, who isn't pleased at all.

"Will you please sit down Jack, we need to do the register."

He wonders if he put his papers in his bag, he can't remember if he put them in.

"**Jack!** Are you listening? **Jack** what have I said?"

"Sorry Mrs Mack, what did you say?"

"I'm doing the register Jack, I needed to know if you were here."

Mrs Smith the TA whispered to her.

"Yes Mrs Mack, I am. I'm not with the fairies like Mrs Smith said," and he smiled at her and wondered if TA meant she was a Terrorist Assistant, but Jack definitely wouldn't say that to her.

Jack's Class

The children are sitting on the carpet, listening to Mrs Mack. Jack tries his best to listen. It is hard to listen and he watches her mouth move at the same time, it looks very funny. He never noticed that spot on her nose before, it's quite big and her ears have nice sparkly earrings on them. Her hair has a big black line down the middle called 'roots'; she must have had it put in like his Mum does.

Mrs Smith is sitting behind him to make sure he is focussed and keeps tapping him on the shoulder or turning his head if he looks out of the window. It sometimes hurts him if she suddenly turns his head quickly. She sometimes puts her hands at either side of his ears to hold him, but that is stupid because then he can't hear.

Mrs Mack is talking but he can't stop watching another class outside. The class are running about, and he keeps getting distracted by the noise and them moving about. Anyway, he's lost track of what Mrs Mack was saying, she talks too fast. He finds it really hard to sit still on the carpet. He fidgets all the time to get comfortable. He sometimes feels really dizzy when he sits still.

If he stares at the blackboard his eyes hurt and sometimes it makes him look like he's crying. He tries to concentrate on the letters but they start to jump about and wiggle, it's really weird.

He is trying his best to keep up to what Mrs Mack is talking about. He thinks she wants him to write a story: he could do this because he could write about the Three Bears or Cinderella because they had written about that loads of times.

He starts thinking about dinosaurs and what they like to eat, maybe he could write about that.

"Jack! Are you listening, what did I just say?" Mrs Mack calls to him, staring intensely.

"I think you need to check what time Jack goes to bed Mrs Mack, he seems to be half asleep," said Mrs Smith twisting Jack's head towards her. "If I have to warn you again Jack you will have time-out, you need to focus."

Jack wasn't bothered really, he had learnt that if you got sent out you didn't have to work and if you stayed in at break it didn't matter because he fell in the playground and no one played with him that much anyway. Anton could waste a whole half an hour and he had special tablets because he couldn't help it. Mrs Mack had once said she thought Jack had ADPMT (or something like that) but his Mum thought that was rubbish because she told her that he was fine at home, it was just school he hated. Jack doesn't think she should have said that. Anyway, his Mum could have that because every few weeks she cleans the house like a 'Tasmanian Devil'. He thinks that's what his Dad called her.

If you really messed about while they sorted out your "inappropriate behaviour" you got out of working for ages. He never got any better though because if he had to stay in at break-time to do his missed work it was still bad because the work was never good enough. The more he wrote the worse his writing got but Mrs Smith kept saying the same stupid thing ~ "Practice makes perfect."

Jack thought she must have practised at being horrible because she was perfect.

"Alright Jack, out you go. Mrs Smith has asked you three times and you've ignored her, five minutes outside to think about your actions."

Jack was taken outside the class and asked to stand against the wall. He could see his bag lying on the floor. He knew his work he had done at home was in there, because he could see it. He went over and took it out to read.

He loved dinosaurs, he was an expert, he knew everything about them, what they ate, how big they were, their names, everything.

"Now then Jack, have you decided what you want to do, are you going to work? What's that you've got there?"

"It's my work I did at home Mrs Mack, it's all about dinosaurs, I thought you would be pleased to see it Mrs Mack."

Mrs Mack knelt down to Jack and looked at him. She couldn't understand how he could do so much work at home. It was different at home, he wasn't rushed; in his bedroom he wasn't disturbed, he could concentrate. On his computer he could use the keypad to write, he hated writing. At school they only went in the ICT room once a week. If Mrs Mack saw him on the computer she would be really impressed; he could "teach her a thing or two", as his Dad was always saying.

At home his Mum and Dad thought he was a genius because he could talk about various topics from history in the 15th century, the Egyptians and especially the prehistoric era. His Dad loved having hours of intelligent conversation while they sat in their quiet area of the conservatory.

He once had to go to the Head Teacher's office for not doing his work and Mr Muppitt had said, "That lad's having you on, he's a clever little monkey; he's just told me all about The Big Bang and evolution, he's not stupid, he's messing about."

Mrs Mack took hold of Jack's hand and took him back into class.

"I want you to write me a story in class, you can write about dinosaurs if you know so much."

Mrs Mack put Jack at a table next to her seat. He doesn't like the school chairs, he can't get comfy; he fiddles and fidgets until he feels right. He can't seem to get his balance on the chair and when he tries to write his legs move about. He wraps his feet around the chair legs or he likes to kneel to stop his legs moving about. He leans over the paper but slips and before he knows it he has fallen, he looks around but no one has seen him. That was lucky! He sits back quickly and wiggles about again, but when he presses his pencil down it snaps. He gets up to get a pencil sharpener.

"Jack, what are you doing?"

"I'm sharpening my pencil Mrs Mack."

Jack goes back to his seat but can see Mrs Smith watching him. He tries to write, but he can never seem to get his hand to hold the pencil right; he holds the pencil like he's going to stab someone because it hurts if he holds it like Mrs Smith says.

Sometimes he feels like stabbing someone but he shouldn't think like that, it's really naughty. But sometimes he gets really angry. If he lies across the desk and writes it's much better. If he writes it makes him sweat because he presses on the pencil so hard.

Jack feels like he is using all his powers like Superman just to write one line. He has to hold on tight just to keep still. No one understands him. No one understands how hard it is. When he does write all the letters are joined up like a big snake.

Mrs Smith is always trying to get him to put his fingers to make a space in between each word. Jack finds it so hard to balance on his chair and twist his fingers to make a space and twist his hand to hold the pencil right.

Jack can spell words like "cat" and "dog" but he sometimes gets them backwards when he writes. He gets his 'w' and 'm' and 'd' and 'p' mixed up because they are the same shape. Longer words are harder and when he reads he sometimes leaves whole lines out. Jack can read well but he is just saying the words and he never remembers what he reads.

Once Mrs Smith tested him by asking him questions about what he had read and he couldn't tell her. He could remember the long words, say them, and could hear his voice, but he wasn't listening to the story. Mrs Smith wasn't interested when he told her, she just thinks he's "not focussing." It's like when he looks at the blackboard, he can't follow the lines of writing properly, they get all muddled up. Mrs Smith thinks he is trying to finish his work quickly.

"Dear me Jack, this will not do. What have I told you? Mrs Mack likes you to sit straight up in your chair, feet down, and tilt the paper sideways. That's better, and don't forget to leave spaces."

Jack knows he can't write like this, it isn't comfortable. Who on earth said you had to write like this? Is there a law that says you have to? It was probably made by people who could write and hadn't any problems. Oh no! It was her, Mrs Smith, she's here; she has come to say her favourite words, "Practice makes perfect Jack."

But Jack knows that it makes him worse, the more writing he does the worse it gets. It's like rubbing a blister, it never gets better. When Jack writes he sometimes writes with his left hand and then swaps to his right hand in the middle to finish the line. If he starts in the middle of the page with his right hand and writes from left to right it is much easier. That really makes Mrs Mack cross; she's always saying, "I wish you wouldn't mess about Jack, you're just showing off."

Jack is trying to sit on the chair without falling ~ hold the pencil correctly ~ think about how to form his letters ~ keep the letters on the line ~ swap hands ~ spell properly ~ mixes up the story because he can't work out the beginning ~ middle or ending ~ has to leave spaces ~ has to put capital letters first ~ for people's names ~ places ~ ughhhhh ~ has to think of a story at the same time ~ he can hear children outside ~ he can see them running ~ George and Annie are talking ~ he can smell buns in Nursery ~ he has to listen to Mrs Mack because she keeps shouting out instructions.

Mrs Mack walks over to Jack and sits down next to him. She leans over and pats his head gently; she can tell he is fed up.

"You love dinosaurs Jack, I just can't understand how you can write like this, I thought it would be gushing out from that clever little brain you have in that handsome little head, what's wrong with you Jack?"

Jack knows she thinks he's lazy, she doesn't say it to him but that's what people think. Mrs Mack said that Angus in his class couldn't help it because he had special needs just like Ben and Megan who were all in his group.

He hated being in that group, that was when he got really fed up because he was on stage 8 for reading and that was brilliant for his age. When he did his group work with the others he answered all the questions first because he read it in his own time, he knew everything, it's just he couldn't write it down fast enough.

"Jack! Are you listening? You're daydreaming again, off you go and have your dinner and play Jack, the fresh air will do you good."

Mrs Smith is watching him in case he runs away with the fairies. Jack sometimes wishes he could. Maybe when his wobbly tooth falls out the tooth fairy will fly him away.

Dinner Time

Jack goes with the rest of the class for his dinner. Everyone is pushing and it's really difficult not to trip or fall over.

Jack tried dinners once but he didn't like them much. The tall lady in the white coat, called "the cook", asked him if he wanted "Mash ~ chips ~ smiley faces ~ peas ~ carrots ~ cabbage ~ pizza with chips ~ sausage and mash ~ pizza and smiley faces ~ gravy on his sausage with peas ~ salad in the salad bar ~ an apple ~ a yogurt ~ jam roly poly and custard ~ raspberry jelly ~ lime jelly…

UGGGHHHH! She got really mad because he just stood there and looked at her with his mouth open, staring at her. He had anything she put on his plate because he couldn't remember it all and she looked mad.

Jack has the same thing every day, he knows what his crisps taste like, the feel, the look, he doesn't like change because the same is safe.

He eats as quickly as he can but he gets told off by Mrs Greece, the dinner lady, for making a mess. Jack's glad he's only eating crisps; he can't seem to judge where his mouth is sometimes and if you give him a knife and fork it's like watching a juggler.

"How on earth can you miss that mouth young Jack? I don't know. Go on, clear off you messy monster!," says Mrs Blunt.

He likes Mrs Blunt, she's always cuddling him and making him laugh when he falls over. She's the third aider, or something like that. Anyway, she's kind. She is always saying, "We'll have to get you a season ticket if you keep coming to me that often my little stunt man," and then she squeezes his "chubby cheeks." She does that a lot.

Jack goes outside; he hates playtime, no one ever plays with him. He likes to play with the younger children as they play baby games and they aren't as fast when they talk and run around.

He hasn't got many friends. Jack can hear kids from his class arguing as he goes out of the door into the sunshine.

"Look, someone has to count. We can't play without a counter for hide and seek, Ben! You do it."

"I will not, don't be so bossy George."

"Emily you count."

"Nope."

"I will," says Jack.

"You can't count Jack." George turns around to speak to Jack.

"I can George."

Jack begs them to let him play, he doesn't play with anyone much, in fact Jack hasn't really got any friends, or even A friend.

They all agree that Jack can play and all run off and leave Jack with his face to the wall counting.

Mrs Greece the dinner lady walks past and asks Jack if he is OK as he looks as though he is upset. She watches him a lot at dinner time because she gets concerned about how lonely he looks most days. She tries her best to encourage the others to play with him but it's hard. She's been on a course to learn about that. Jack has heard Mrs Blunt saying she was a PIP worker now.

"Look Jack, here's Billy. Billy, do you want to play tig with Jack? Of course you do; go on, off you go."

Jack runs around trying to catch Billy and he is fine until, whoops, there he goes! Over he falls. Mrs Greece runs over to him, she's used to seeing Jack fall, he is so clumsy. She takes Jack in to clean his hands and knees. He cries a lot because he gets fed up, kids get fed up, it isn't just grown ups. Jack knows adults get fed up paying bills and having to do ironing because his Mum is always telling him, but growing up is really hard.

By the time Mrs Greece has calmed Jack down and brought him outside again the bell is going to let the children know it is the end of dinner time. Mrs Mack stands staring at her class who are lining up, wondering why the line is so short.

"Where are all the children Beth?"

Oh No! Jack forgot to go and look for the children, they must be still hiding around the school.

PE

Jack hates PE. He does everything possible to avoid it, he tries suspected broken limbs, no PE kit, the dog ate his shorts and died, applies wet paper towels and cries with tummy ache but, unless he has a note, he has to do it. When he goes on holiday his Mum and Dad love happy hour, but this is Jack's unhappy hour.

At least Mrs Smith isn't here because Mrs Mack said at register that she had gone on a course, thank goodness. Mrs Mack is stood at the door waiting for them to get undressed but Jack is still looking for his PE kit.

"You do this every time Jack, you can't remember where your bag is. Have you a suspected broken arm or leg? What is it today then Jack?"

"I fell at dinner time."

Mrs Mack takes hold of Jack and looks at him. "Look Jack, just do PE in your underpants and vest, you'll be alright, just come in to the hall when you're ready, I'll leave Tom to help you otherwise you will be all day."

Jack takes ages to get undressed. Tom tries his best to help him, but they look more like they are wrestling than getting undressed. Mrs Mack keeps going in to check that he's alright and keeps telling them to stop messing. It's even harder getting your clothes off, and then he knows he will have to start all over again and put them back on.

In Year 1 Mrs Brook made him cry every time he had PE because she refused to put his clothes on because he was just a "lazy, lazy boy and at his age he could dress himself," and she would announce this to the whole class.

He drops his clothes on the floor because he can't fold them like Peter does, all neatly like a soldier does. Jack won't remember which were his anyway as his clothes are all over the place now. Anyway, he's always last so his clothes will be the last ones on the floor. That will get Mrs Mack really cross.

He eventually goes into the hall and Mrs Mack tells him that they are playing traffic lights.

Red for stop ~ green for go ~ orange for OH! he can't remember.

The children start running around and Jack tries his best not to bump into them. Mrs Mack shouts something but he can't hear and then he realises that everyone is standing still. He stops.

They start to run, he is running around, WEEEEEE! OH! they've stopped. They start again and this time he's got lots of space. OH! they are lying down.

"OK! Jack, you're messing around. Every time I ask you to change you're messing about. Sit down Jack, you're not listening at all."

Jack sits down on the bench and he can feel the children staring at him, talking about him. He's trying not to cry but it's really hard not to.

He hates PE, he can't run, he can't catch a ball, he falls, he trips. Oh! He hates it. Jack sobs, great spitty sobs, all the way from his boots.

Mrs Mack asks them all to change and Jack knows he is going to be told off again, and he is. He tries his best but he struggles with his clothes as usual and when he eventually finishes dressing his clothes are inside out, back to front and unfastened.

"Jack! Fasten your shoes," says Mrs Mack, looking flustered and annoyed with him as usual.

"I've tried Mrs Mack but I can't, I need some help," looking up at Mrs Mack with his tearful, fed–up, I want to go home look.

"I don't know Jack, what will we do with you?"

Mrs Mack is always saying the same things every day; he never seems to get better at anything.

Before he knows it Mrs Mack says it's home time. Jack can see his Mum in the playground. He runs as fast as he can to her, knocking anyone in the way, he's safe now his Mum's there.

"Come on my little Bambi," she shouts to him as he runs with his hands and legs flapping about.

He is so happy to see his Mum, he's had an awful day.

"Don't run too fast Jack you'llllllllll fallllllllllll! OH! JACK! There you go again!"

Miracles

Jack went to school that week, nothing changed much in class apart from Mrs Smith not being there. Jack was really happy because Mrs Smith always watched him and it made him worry.

He had a lovely weekend with his Mum and Dad. He loved weekends and holidays because it was when he was the most happy. If he was not at school, he was as happy as a pig in a pigsty. Jack had gone to his Nana's and taken Bert, her dog, for a walk. His Dad had flown his kite in the field next to his Nana's house and then they had gone for a long walk.

On Sunday they got up late and he went on the internet and looked up the most amazing information on 'The Big Bang' ~ how the earth was formed millions of years ago ~ evolution ~ mankind ~ it just was so interesting Jack didn't want the weekend to finish and his brain was just so full of useful information.

Jack hated Mondays, he knew he would have days of horrible school ahead, if only he could remember the days of the week in order. His Mum walked him into school and he could see Mrs Smith waving at his Mum.

"You-hoo! Mrs McCrory."

Oh No! What has Jack done now? It must be bad because they are whispering in a corner and they look serious.

Jack stands against the wall waiting for his Mum to come over, she will be cross and he will be made to have consequences for his behaviour or be grounded.

Mrs Smith and his Mum walk over and bend down to Jack. They're smiling. Jack is really worried, they've never looked like this before, and they look scary.

Mrs Smith holds Jack's hand and looks into his eyes.

"Jack, Mrs Mack has asked your Mum to come and have a chat with her and me after school. I don't want you to think you're in trouble because you're not. You go into school and I'll be in soon and don't worry, everything is fine now my little pet."

Jack walks into school staring with his mouth open. He turns to wave at his Mum who is watching him with Mrs Smith, they're smiling and waving at him.

Mrs Smith is giving her a book.

Something is wrong, something is very wrong, he must have a serious disease and he's going to die and they are going to break it to him gently ~ or his Dad has died ~ or his gerbil Stanley or Bert his Nana's dog. OH MY GIDDY AUNT!

Or maybe they are going to move to Outer Mongolia and he will never have to go to school again and that's why Mrs Smith is so pleased. It means that praying every night to God with his Ted has saved him.

Mrs Smith comes into the cloakroom and helps Jack take his coat off and puts his coat and bag on his peg.

"Look Jack, your peg is at the end of the wall now near the door, and I have put a dinosaur picture there now so you will remember. I know you can read really well but this will be easier."

She walks into the classroom with her hand behind his back, gently guiding him in and helping him to sit on a chair.

He looks confused, he feels confused, and Mrs Mack is smiling at him with her head to one side.

Mrs Mack does the register and Mrs Smith reminds Jack when it is his turn. She's never done that. She's never spoken to him without sounding cross.

They listen to a story and Jack keeps looking at Mrs Mack but she just smiles back at him. After a while Mrs Smith asks if Jack will go out with her because she wants to do some things with him. She tells him not to worry as it won't hurt and they will have fun. He's never had fun with Mrs Smith.

They go into the library where it's quiet and Mrs Smith asks Jack to take his shoes and socks off while she makes a space by moving the furniture around. Jack is really worried now because he is struggling to get his shoes and socks off and Mrs Smith is helping him.

"Now then Jack, I would like you to copy me. I would like you to walk up to this line on your tiptoes like this."

She showed him what to do and he belly laughed because she looked really silly. Mrs Smith laughed as well as she tripped up and fell against the bookshelf.

Mrs Smith showed him how to walk on his heels ~ to walk on the inside of his feet and the outsides. She looked really silly. All the time she wrote things down on a piece of paper.

He laughed loads, He had never heard Mrs Smith laugh before ~ she's really funny ~ and she laughs like his Granddad.

He did lots of different things and she said he was brilliant, he didn't like to tell her that she looked really stupid but she's quite old and old people do look silly a lot when they're over 20, that's very old. Jack wondered if she remembered dinosaurs.

When he had finished Mrs Smith took him back to the class and said, "Can you write me a story Jack McCrory?" She was smiling a massive smile.

She said it didn't matter what he wrote, it could be anything. He wrote about the Three Bears because he knew that story off by heart and it was easy. It wasn't very good but Mrs Smith said it was brilliant and that he had tried his best. He knew there must be something going on now because she never said that.

Mrs Smith followed him around all day, keeping her eye on him, it was spooky. They did PE and she helped him get undressed and dressed, she just smiled when he ran around. If he fell over or bumped into the others she looked at Mrs Mack and smiled and just said, "Up you get Jack, keep going, you're doing fine."

"They've both had brain transplants, they must have done, they're not acting the same, I'm not getting on their nerves, I'm not a nuisance, I know I am," he thought.

After school his Mum, Mrs Mack and Mrs Smith all go into the class and Jack is really worried now as he has been asked to join them. They are all staring at him.

Mrs Mack started talking first. "Jack, I have asked your Mum to come and have a chat because we think we know why you find school so difficult. First of all, Mrs Smith has been on a course last week and they taught her how to help you and other children. Mrs Smith says there are a few other children that she can help as well. That's what she was doing today with you in the library and she said you had some fun in there."

Jack nodded and just kept staring at them all smiling at him.

"Anyway," said Mrs Smith, "I would just like to say how sorry I am Jack for letting you struggle for so long, because now we know what your difficulties are we can help you, from now on we are here to help you."

For the first time Jack looked at Mrs Smith and she looked quite nice really. She looked a bit sad and her eyes were watery like when his Mum watches a really soppy film at home. That's when he and his Dad are told to shut up and go away. Not in a polite way though.

The adults talked for ages and Jack's Mum put him on her knee and cuddled him while they talked. For the first time ever he felt happy in school.

2. Mrs Smith the Support Assistant

I call myself Mrs Smith, but I am a thousand Mrs Smiths out there, working every day supporting children in mainstream schools. Jack is a mixture of children and their difficulties that I have worked with, all rolled into one small child. I have written comments I have said as a support assistant and conversations I have heard from other people.

Mrs Smith is unable to help or understand Jack and shows the emotion and frustration (exaggerated) that I experienced so many times supporting children like Jack. Children with Jack's problems can try your patience over the years because, like Mrs Smith, I was ignorant to their difficulties. But, for the majority of staff, we do the job because we love children and care enough to find ways of supporting them to enable them to fulfil their potential.

The day I went on a course for dyspraxia and how to screen children changed my life completely.

If I was being really truthful, when I applied for the course it was the prospect of a day out away from the stresses of school with a free dinner thrown in that appealed to me more. I was desperate for a break. A lot of courses are booked with the catering facilities being a priority. The consideration of the content of refreshments and lunches rather than the content of the courses is very important and if anybody says it isn't they are fibbing.

As a professional I should say I was doing it to enhance my learning and my personal development.

Taking 12 weeks to support a child who was also labelled a "chair chucker" to stay on task for five minutes to write their name and chanting like a mantra "It is not my teaching ability it is their learning ability," a hundred times a day, you begin to look forward to days off.

To me, dyspraxia was something you went to the doctors about because it was a medical condition which affected your body. Following a referral from your doctor you saw an Occupational Therapist who then took control and you were sorted; it was nothing to do with school.

I was shocked, and realised how ignorant I was, because the day I attended the course about dyspraxia was the day I found the missing piece to a puzzle I had been trying to find for years. I had worked with special needs children with varying degrees of difficulties in behaviour and learning for what seemed a lifetime. If you worked it out, I had probably spent longer with these children than my own. I was so engrossed in the course that I didn't want any lunch; I just wanted to get back and listen.

The course not only told you about dyspraxia and how to screen children, but it explained about the benefits of exercises and how to implement an exercise programme based on the Madeleine Portwood book. I listened, and all the time I could see children that I worked with, or had worked with, appearing in my thoughts. The worst thing was seeing my own son's face and things that he had done and words I had said to him. When I write about Jack's Mum, it's me talking, my ignorance of not knowing my son's difficulties and my frustrations. I hope I was never that bad tempered but that's what guilt does to you and I wish I could turn the clock back.

I love my son but he hated school all those years ago. He was diagnosed as having dyslexia, but I now know that dyspraxia was the root cause.

I believed the experts because I was ignorant and taught by my parents to respect authority. My son was never as bad as Jack and it was only his handwriting that was his difficulty. I have portrayed Jack as an extreme.

I couldn't wait to get back to school the next day: in fact I couldn't sleep. I just kept going over in my mind about the course and what had been said. The first child I kept seeing in my thoughts was a child in Year 2 and, sure enough, he was one of the first children to be screened and to start the programme.

Immediately I arranged to see our Special Educational Needs Coordinator,(SENCO) who, thank goodness, listened to everything I had to say and that was it, we were both on a mission!

I told her about everything on the course and the children with the characteristics of dyspraxia. I knew immediately that it was the group of children that I worked with.

All the children I supported were in Year 2 and, when I screened them, I was quite shocked. On the course the Tutor had demonstrated how to screen children using the Madeleine Portwood method and we were shown how to screen each other.

We were adults without any difficulties, apart from myself who had a dodgy knee and wobbled (due to playing out with my children sledging at Christmas). I was oblivious to the realisation of how their difficulties showed up and, in some cases, they were quite distressing.

The first thing you ask the children to do is for them to walk on their tiptoes forward and then, without turning, walk backwards.

You are looking all the time to see if their hands turn down, (mirroring their feet) as this shows that messages are going to every part of the body. Most of them were fine doing this but the next exercise was walking on their heels. They all turned their hands up and I thought, "This is fine, this is what we have been taught, no problem."

But the next time, I asked a child to walk on the inside and outside of his feet. His body was completely twisted trying to walk back, his face contorted and his tongue sticking out, straining to walk back to me. It was very hard not to get emotional. I remember another TA watching me looking worried as I said, "Well done, that was brilliant." When you know how difficult that was for them it is heartbreaking. The only consolation I have is that, when I screen children, I know there is real hope and it is very rare that most children show such severe signs.

At that time I had no idea how the exercises would work. In fact, to say I was panicking a bit at that point, and thinking I might have taken on a bit too much, was putting it mildly.

After I had screened 12 children we chose six to start the programme. At the time I just put the others on a list for the next programme, thinking it would be alright for them to wait. Now I know that every day waiting means those children are struggling in class. At the time we didn't know the impact it would have on the children, they were our guinea pigs. But at least we were trying to do something.

Starting with gross and fine motors skills, I picked at random various exercises that looked interesting. I photocopied page after page thinking, "Ooooo that looks nice," but really I hadn't got a clue as there were hundreds that looked interesting.

Meanwhile I read book after book that our SENCO kept ordering to help me understand dyspraxia and all the areas it affected.

Most of the books I couldn't understand because the words were far too long and most of the time I couldn't say them anyway.

The books gave you research and stories with evidence and drawings, they gave you graphs and percentages and some gave you research into the possible origin of dyspraxia.

Was dyspraxia caused because it was hereditary or because of nutrition and the lack of fish oils?

I wasn't bothered about statistics and how to deal with symptoms; I needed to overcome the illness.

No book tells you how to arrange the whole school's timetable, so that no one has the use of the hall from 9.00am until 9.30am, without someone getting upset, because Tuesday's Year 5 have always done PE and Wednesday's Year 6 practice recorder; Mrs Brook always has it on a Thursday, and what if book club wants to set up? And anyway, what is dyspraxia? No one has told the staff about it and why was I a priority all of a sudden?

No one tells you that you have to wait until the SENCO tells all the staff what you are doing. When you are so eager to get started you have to wait for a staff meeting. My school was very supportive, but a lot of schools cannot see beyond the inconvenience and refuse to adjust to what was (I can see now) quite a risk.

Parents were asked to come in and discuss their children's difficulties and our programme. Most parents were very supportive as we explained to them how we had screened their children and they had shown difficulties in their motor skills, impacting on their education.

Some parents couldn't understand how they could have missed such difficulties and were very upset. Some cried in the meeting, which I understood as this was the reaction I had when I was told my son had dyslexia.

No one tells you in a book how to deal with parents who are upset, that total feeling of despair.

At home most things very rarely change on a daily basis. Children have processed information they need to know at home, they can move around and feel comfortable. The house is the same: rooms, furniture and toys. They do everything at their pace. The atmosphere is totally different; they have the quiet corners they can escape to.

At school they are constantly bombarded with new information, new instructions that they have to process quickly. They change classrooms and move. People change, clothes change, they have to go out doors and in, they have to take coats on or off. Even hair changes, because girls can have a different hairstyle every day. Alice had pigtails yesterday and today she looks different because she has a ponytail and is wearing jeans.

On top of this, children have to learn to read, write, spell, draw, history, geography, UGHHHH! Conform to all the rules that are made, even though they can't remember them, and behave.

Then you have the parents who are in denial because they don't believe there is a problem. When you are a parent, you plan goals and have milestones that your child will achieve and, if someone tells you they won't, it spoils those plans. Some children don't go at a pace their parents want and some children stop a little and need help.

Some parents have to blame school because their babies were alright until you got your hands on them, it must be your teaching ability, not their little dumpling's learning ability.

Other parents feel guilty because they think it is their fault. My daughter said it wasn't my fault she had failed her driving test and I couldn't blame myself for everything. It wasn't because I hadn't emphasised the green cross code more when she was little.

Then there are the parents who blame themselves for not spotting it because they had to work and they were too busy.

Also, I am sure parents thought, "Who is she diagnosing my child with dyspraxia? She's only a support assistant," and that is what you never do. You never tell a parent, "Your child has dyspraxia."

I am not qualified to diagnose dyspraxia, although the person who implemented the course was an Educational Psychologist, and a parent who uses exercises at home isn't qualified. The worst thing about saying "dyspraxia" is that most parents go on to the internet or read a book and come up with severe dyspraxia. This immediately presses every panic button as it gives you information about the worst cases imaginable. It lists everything and you never think your child may just have one difficulty or a few. Parents of course always think the worst; I know I do.

Then you have the parents who hug you and tell you how glad they are that someone has admitted there is a problem and they are at last doing something about it. For years they had known there was a problem and no one would commit themselves. They have met with every professional and agency. They were beginning to think they were just fussy parents.

This is when parents walk out of the room and you know you have lifted a weight off their shoulders and they will sleep a little better that night. The first time it happened in the early years it made me worried because parents had put such trust and faith in us to make a difference in their lives. At the time I was completely unsure of what the children could achieve even though I believed in it.

Parents were given forms to fill in to give us permission to start the programmes and we agreed to start after the Christmas holidays. I was really excited and I couldn't wait, everything was ready. The exercises had been chosen.

Again, no one tells you in a book how to collect the resources needed without being a nuisance because classes may need them every day and you have to put things back. Or, if you eventually get resources of your own, where do you actually store them as schools have very limited space?

Then the grumpy old caretaker appears just as you have marked the hall with white masking tape. He taps you on the back, as you have just measured your line precisely and struggled to position it, and tells you, "You can't put that down on my floor, I've just polished and buffed."

Eventually, after weeks of negotiations with Hitler, you manage to convince him to let you leave tape down. You arrive triumphantly the next day only to discover that it has been picked off by various children sitting on the floor in assembly.

I had planned and produced on the computer the exercises we had decided to do. Each child was to be monitored closely with their screening first, then some written work before the programme, and then we would ask the children to write something after six weeks. This would enable us to compare their work and see if the children had made progress. They all had their own files and worksheets to monitor their difficulties and change the exercises.

This was put in a new blue file marked

Motor Skills Difficulties Monitoring and Assessment

I must have fallen off a narny tree!

The first exercise was jumping with both feet together between a measured line and then hopping on the left leg and then the right leg. After that we had turning a skipping rope with a partner, throwing a ball and then they had to play a glockenspiel four times on each bar. I thought it would be nice because it would help with their fine motor skills and co-ordination and anyway, I thought it would sound nice.

Everything was set out for them in the hall for the first day and the Year 2 class teacher had been given a list of all the children who would be on the programme. The majority of staff agreed that it was worth trying as most of the children were missing out in class anyway because of their difficulties. I know there was the odd one who was dubious but they never said. To be honest, none of us really knew if it would work, but the more I read, the more it made sense.

3.   The 'A' Team

The children chosen to start the programme were all from Year 2 and all had varying degrees of difficulties.

Amy was six and a bit years old and was a brilliant artist. She could draw with the skill most artists would kill for. Amy wasn't someone you would have thought of immediately, because of her ability with her fine motors, but I was aware of other difficulties and started to look at the whole picture. I screened her because of her gross motor and social difficulties.

Working in a care club after school, I would watch Amy drawing and writing for hours. We tried everything to get her to play with the other children but she was happy to sit at her little table and produce mountains of paper work. We always joked that she would marry WH Smith's son when she got older. The real problem for Amy was that she struggled to follow instructions and would always be the last to sit down and appeared to "be away with the fairies." Amy would also come up with the most incredible excuses to avoid doing PE and would almost certainly have received an Oscar for the category of best actress award. In fact, thinking about PE, all the children who had been chosen could have joined the local thespian group.

The next was George, who was the baby of the group. This was not because of his age but because he was dinky and you wanted to mother him. Or sometimes you felt like you could "smother him" as he was like a performing jumping flea. He never sat still long enough to write, draw, listen, follow instructions, had no sense of danger but looked like an angel and charmed you into submission. He was the nearest you would get to Jack. George was unable to write and form even his name fully, although if he could spell and write "pest" that would have been sufficient. He wasn't interested in writing because he hadn't time, it was boring.

Then we had Maisy, who had been diagnosed by an Educational Psychologist as having everything that you could possibly catch. She had dyspraxia, dyslexia and dyscalcula (or was it culia?) and Maisy knew all about "the three D's" as her parents had explained the whole caboodle to her. In fact, the day I sat all the children down, Maisy was the one who became the teacher. She put it in a way that they understood. It wasn't how the books would have said it but they were happy and anyway, Maisy spoke in a way children could understand because she was a child. I am not afraid to admit this, but the fact is Maisy was "very articulate" gave her more of an advantage than me for public speaking.

"You see, in your brain you have wires that send messages to your body to do things. Most children's wires are all straight but ours are all in a mess, a bit like spaghetti. Mrs Smith is going to untangle all the mess and it will help us all to do our work better and, if we're lucky, our bodies will be so fit we will be able to win a gold medal for our country in the Olympics."

Some of them seemed highly delighted at the prospect of me training them to be potential gold medal winners and it seemed to boost their low self-esteem. Others hadn't quite understood or processed the implications and goals she was setting me. I knew her parents always supported her and told her she was good at everything, just to keep her going, but this was definitely putting the pressure on me big time now. Nevertheless, it made my pages of planned complicated speech about strengthening their neural pathways completely over the top and they were happy.

I have tried on other occasions to give children a more in–depth explanation of the reasons why we do the exercises and the impact it will have on them as I felt it was my duty to do this.

Children are not interested; they want to be able to write better and catch a ball or play football better. In Maisy's case it was to dance like a prima ballerina, because Maisy was always dancing. She would flit and float around at any opportunity: the only thing is, she had no balance or direction, no co-ordination or rhythm. To be in the same room as Maisy when she danced was dangerous.

Maisy was in my small group in Year 2 and could draw the most beautiful pictures of princesses with the most detail you had ever seen. Impressive, you may think, but Maisy drew this picture all through the planned National Curriculum lessons at any opportunity. This was Maisy's avoidance strategy and her achievement in life. She could write a few words to make a sentence but struggled to make any progress and every intervention and support was failing. She was a still a princess and her parents had tried everything in their power to support her.

Maisy had seen every professional and had endured every test available to be diagnosed. Her parents were thrilled that Maisy was to be part of the programme as they had researched every area of dyspraxia to help Maisy and understood the importance of the exercises. They fully supported us and went away happy, making our job a lot easier I thought. Much later, her Mum confessed that she was one of the brave faces that cried in the comfort of her own home.

That's three children so far. The next was James who had been supported at every opportunity with every teaching resource possible but nothing had worked. He also chose to play with the fairies, the naughty elves and goblins and tripped and fell on a regular basis. James also fought daily with his Mum to get to school, to enter school, to stay in school. He hated school.

Then we had "Stormin Norman." Now he was a challenge! He never followed instructions and he was always in the corridor for time-out because he was there to try your patience. He was a child like Jack, who I would continually ask to focus and wonder if he had slept at all the night before as he was permanently half asleep. Whatever you told him he would have forgotten within five minutes, if you could get him to stay still long enough for you to tell him. He never sat on his bottom but continually lolled about the floor.

On the course we were shown evidence of a child's handwriting, which was a continuous snake with no spaces. That was how Norman wrote and I was delighted that we had at last found out what was wrong with him. I must admit, following that course I did a lot of head patting, saying "sorry", feeling guilty, saying "Ah bless", and feeling compassion for these children, instead of the impatience and frustration I had felt for years.

I had also stopped swearing as much under my breath and stopped my friends thinking I had Tourettes Syndrome.

We mustn't forget Katie, who was the quiet one. Even though she showed difficulties with her motor skills, I think I chose this little girl because I thought I would have at least one child who would give me an easy time. She was no trouble in class because she never made a fuss.

You immediately thought of Katie when you thought of a child with gross motor difficulties. Katie did PE but never liked it, she never cried when she was asked to do anything, you just knew she would never manage it, she would just accept her fate. You would haul her up onto a bench and ask her to walk along it. She would stand, too terrified to move forward. If she attempted to ascend the climbing frame, you would have to prise her fingers from the bars as she had wrapped around it like a koala bear, even though she was only one step up. When you looked away, she would be in front of 20 children waiting for her to jump off the bench.

The teacher would give up after 10 minutes because of her adamant refusal to move and her vice-like grip: her nails digging into your arms and thighs were leaving marks. When she was asked to roll along the mat she would roll sideways into the kitchen and you would have to drag her back by the legs (gently of course, within Social Services guidelines and Health and Safety requirements).

Katie was friendly to everyone but at playtime she would only join in if it was a still game; like Jack, she knew she would fall. Katie also went to care club and liked to watch TV or draw. When I think about it, I can't remember Katie ever running around outside in the playground; she would sit and talk to herself quietly under the tree.

I went down to collect my little guinea pigs but had to wait because George and James were late, as usual. My stomach was churning as I knew I only had 30 minutes to get them into the hall and do the programme. As they arrived at the door five minutes late I grabbed them and whisked their coats off. They were escorted (pushed and pulled gently) into the hall. As they all gathered together I asked them to take their shoes and socks off. I went over and got my file and pen out and looked around. They were all sat there.

"Can you take your shoes and socks off please."

"My Mum does that Mrs Smith."

"So does mine."

"And mine."

Norman was at this point up the climbing frame and Katie was just looking at me with that look of "I don't think so."

I retrieved Norman and held on to him as I asked him to stay by my side. I started with Maisy and told the others to start trying to take their shoes off and I would get around to helping them.

Katie had tights on so I sent her behind the curtains, only to get her back out because it was dark and she had fallen. As her tights were around her ankles at this point, I pulled them gently until they were off. "YES!"

James was struggling so I helped him next. George had mountain boots on with 50 holes in and 10 foot of laces. I had my head down helping him when I realised that Norman was up the apparatus again. I grabbed him down and held on to him again as I concentrated on Amy who hadn't moved and was flying to Neverland with Tinkerbell. I undid her buckles and looked at Norman who was stood with his shoes and socks in his hands. Norman had Velcro shoes; thank goodness there is a God.

"What a good boy you are Norman, my little star."

Norman looked confused.

Mrs Chaviss poked her head around the curtains to ask if she could have James for her reading group as it was 9.30am.

I could feel a Tourette's moment coming on…

4.   If at first you don't succeed...

I made my apologies to the class teacher and carried on with my jobs for the day, but I kept going over in my mind about that awful morning.

Here were six children who I couldn't control; in 30 minutes I had been reduced to helplessness. It was time to have a plan of action if I was going to survive. I would go in and take their shoes and socks off for them because here were children who struggled with their motor skills and I was asking them to perform a simple task and they couldn't do it.

So I will do it, quick sticks, sorted.

The next day I collected them from their class and quickly directed them into the hall. I sat them in a line on the benches and proceeded to whip their shoes and socks off in military fashion. It took five minutes, which was brilliant; apart from Norman who had disappeared up the apparatus like a bat out of hell.

I retrieved him and then looked around and Amy and James were at the other side of the hall now. Katie had wrapped herself around the curtains like a cocoon and was wailing. George was in a trance, oblivious to any of it. I shouted to them, as the noise they were making was horrendous, as I dragged Katie out.

"Ok! I want you to jump with your feet together five times, then I want you to jump on your left foot and then your right, then we are going to skip and following that we will play some really nice music."

Nothing happened for 30 seconds and then they all started to move around. Maisy and Amy looked like they were auditioning for River Dance (but badly) and kept falling to the floor. Norman was up the apparatus again. George was doing his impression of a Tasmanian devil.

"Stop!" I shouted as loud as I could and they all looked at me. "Come here, over here to me, I want you to come over here right now."

What on earth was going on here? I was losing control again.

Then of course, it dawned on me; was I stupid, for goodness sake? I realised that I would have to change the way I spoke to them. Here were children who didn't have good motor skills (dressing/undressing, balance, direction and co-ordination) and who didn't process information quickly (follow instructions). They had very different needs and personalities.

Norman and Maisy were confident in themselves but most of the others were unsure of both me and the programme.

I had to be clearer and not rabbit on, as it was too much for them to process. I was rushing them to fit in with a school timetable. But then wasn't that the same every day for these children? They always had to go at a pace they couldn't keep up with.

I took George by the hand and led him to the white lines that were marked out. "Stay here George."

I took Katie by the hand and led her to George. "Don't move."

I led Amy and Maisy, retrieved Norman from his nest on the climbing frame, and grabbed James. I put them in order at the beginning of the white line and asked them to stay still until I told them to move.

I walked backwards so that I could keep my eye on them and gave them my instructions: "George jump to me with both feet." He set off with his back bent, head down and arms flapping. His feet shuffled until he fell in front of me.

It was awful as I picked him up and sent him back to the others. "Didn't George do well? Come on Katie, your turn."

Katie tiptoed quietly with her arms flapping as well, a bit like a pigeon that's had too much seed. "That was brilliant Katie."

Norman was next. He flapped his arms and hands and his tongue stuck out the side of his face. He kept going until his legs gave way. He got straight back up and had another go until the end, but he finished. He punched the air and gave a triumphant " Yes!" as he strutted off.

I clapped like a seal in a circus. "That was great Norman, well done."

Maisy was next and did all the hand and arm flapping but with grace. She shuffled to me and said, "Oh! Mrs Smith, that really was rather terrible wasn't it?"

"That was brilliant Maisy, really."

"Oh! Thank you so much Mrs Smith, I love your outfit you're wearing by the way," and she went and joined the queue. I liked that girl; she had class.

Amy didn't flap as much but her back was bent over until she fell.

"Up you get Amy." But she didn't look happy.

James jumped once and then his legs went with a wobble, he tried again and they went and wobbled ~ he went and wobbled ~ went and wobbled until he had finished.

They all did two more sets of jumps and that was enough: they couldn't have done any more, they were exhausted.

I was supposed to have achieved at least 10 to 15 exercises that day but taking shoes and socks off and jumping feet together would have to do.

The next day was going to be different because I was on a mission now. I had spent at least half an hour yesterday dinner time filling in their observation sheets on what they had achieved. I wrote 'A' in the box if they had achieved the exercise or 'W/T' if they were working towards it. There was no box for taking socks and shoes off. I wrote 'W/T' in the first box to show we had at least accomplished something.

Completing the paperwork was one part of my major plan that I was not going to achieve whilst working with the children. It was impossible to write and control children at the same time.

This was going to take a lot longer than I had imagined. Call me stupid but I had this vision of the children lining up *every* day and achieving *every* exercise with perfection. I would then bring on the next group of children and so it would go on.

"STUPID"

I collected my little guinea pigs from the class and they all looked really happy to see me. I didn't take this as a sign of affection, more of a gesture of relief from them knowing they were getting out of lessons. As Jack had done on numerous occasions, these children's ultimate goal was to avoid anything to do with education.

I was learning fast and as we entered the hall I manoeuvred Norman on to the bench in front of me and blocked him with my body. I was determined to stop his pathway to freedom up the apparatus. They took their shoes and socks off and were guided to make a line at the beginning of the marked floor. Norman was placed at the front and was asked to be the leader: my thinking was that if he was given responsibility it would take his mind off his escape plans. It was his job also to count how many times they had jumped. We were aiming for three times with feet together and maybe a hop, but I wasn't pushing my luck.

They jumped three times and it was much the same as yesterday, with their wings flapping. Norman kept counting but I had this awful feeling we had done a few more than three as he said "Two times jumped" twice. They all kept wandering off and I kept bringing them back, all of them kept going into a trance and I kept shouting to them to go next. If they weren't daydreaming they would be chatting and would have completely forgotten what they were supposed to be doing. They sat down, they chatted, they daydreamed, and all the time I tried to get them to jump.

I eventually asked them all to line up as we were going to hop on the left foot but here we had six children who didn't know their left and right. Here we go again…

I stood and shouted, "The left leg, no this one, no that one, no you've put that one down, YES! NO!"

Norman eventually came towards me, hopped twice then crumpled to the floor. "I can't do this one Mrs Smith, me leg goes."

I went over to him, grabbed under his arm and lifted him up; he was quite a meaty little chap.

I stood at the side and tapped James's right leg to be lifted so that he would know which leg to jump. He went off like a bat out of hell with his arms turning around at each side to get take off.

Norman started shouting, "Go Mr Helicopter Go!" and all the children started laughing.

"Well done James, that was brilliant," as he staggered back.

Maisy flapped and flipped gracefully but she didn't fall. Neither did George, but they had all flapped. Katie had to be lifted along and she too was quite "substantial", as my Dad would have said.

Amy just looked at me with this awful glare and took off flapping and straining and making the most awful noise.

We never finished the next two, but again they were exhausted and it was time to go.

We continued for two weeks with the jumping and hopping until they were able to do three sets of jumping and hopping. They still talked and were easily distracted but Norman had completely surprised me in that he had taken the responsibility of counting very seriously. He would hop first and then go back to remind the others which leg to lift up and then rush to help me lift them up.

We had decided to try and use the skipping ropes today and I had tied the ropes to the apparatus as directed by the book. I had positioned the children into their places and asked them to start, and start they certainly did! They didn't turn the ropes in a 360° circle like you would have expected. They just whipped from side to side. Katie and Amy were screaming as the ropes lashed them from side to side. The boys thought this was great and kept cracking their whips like circus ringmasters.

I immediately stopped them and undid the ropes.

"Sit down and stay on the benches," I yelled, trying not to sound too much as if I had lost control.

I took hold of Maisy and placed the skipping rope in her hand. I then stood her just enough away from me so that she could turn the skipping rope with me. I asked her to make a big circle with her arm holding the skipping rope. Maisy did a complete circle beautifully.

Just at that moment our SENCO walked into the hall. "How are you doing?" she asked.

The children were staring at me with their mouths open, as I kept turning the rope behind me and chatting.

"Mrs Smith!" Norman was shouting as I turned the rope.

"Norman, I am ignoring you if you shout out at me."

I tried to carry on but the children were all jumping up and down and pointing behind me.

"What is wrong with all of you?" I asked, as I turned around to see Maisy with the rope wrapped around her neck and hand as I was reeling her silently towards with me.

"I am so sorry Maisy, you were doing so well," I said as I rushed over to her. I unwrapped her from her bondage and sat her down on the bench.

Maisy was "absolutely fine" but I had had enough as I dressed the children and we finished for the day.

When it says in the book that you "have to monitor the amount of skips before they lose control," this is not what I think they had in mind.

I was learning fast that at no point was I to take my eyes off them, whatever.

5.   Miracles *do* happen

Before I knew it, we were on week three and we had progressed onto other exercises. The children were endeavouring to walk along a white line on the way back to jumping and hopping.

They said in the book that this would help with balance, foot-eye co-ordination. I was supposed to put two lines down and they were to walk between them, but I didn't dare put any more tape on the floor so I had used only one line.

They were like tightrope walkers in a circus as they all tried desperately to walk along the line. They wobbled with their arms and hands still flapping. Two of them clenched their fists and their tongues twisted out of their mouths.

Norman was instructed to start the exercise by walking "heel on toe" until I realised that the queue had stopped and he was standing with his heel on his toes and was unable to move.

"Miss, I'm stuck."

I again realised that at all times these little people must be shown precisely what to do. Katie, George and James also kept walking on their toes and Amy walked sideways: it was really funny to watch.

I don't think I should have told them to imagine that they were walking the plank over a sea of sharks as it was making them more nervous than they should have been.

I don't want to sound as though I was sadistic; I was only trying to make it fun. If anyone walked past as I was doing the exercises I was very conscious of the way I spoke to the children. Over the weeks I had changed my language towards the children, and I don't mean I had stopped swearing. I had realised that the children responded to me with as little information as possible given to them in one time.

When these children are in class and you give them an instruction, it can take a while to process and they can (as Jack did) be thought to be ignoring you.

I would shout "1, 2, 3!" which meant "Stop, look at me and stand still." This worked brilliantly until I played a ball game with another group one day and had given all the children numbers. They were making too much noise and I needed their attention so I shouted "1, 2, 3!" and numbers 1, 2 and 3 threw their balls at me all at once.

I knew that instructions would have to be simple and direct: "Sit down, stop, jump, hop." To anyone who didn't know the reason why I was doing the exercises, I must have sounded like a horrible, stern disciplinarian, but it worked and the children actually liked it. They knew what they had to do, it was quick and direct, no delayed lengthy processing information.

The children now held beanbags in their hands to help them stop their flapping and this seemed to be working. They could all jump and hop on both legs. None of them showed any signs of weakness in either leg and they did the exercises and then went on to the next. They would take it in turns to turn the skipping rope with me. Maisy and Katie could turn it together as they could do a full 360° 30 times without stopping. We never got around to the musical instruments but had progressed to throwing beanbags into a hoop from a marked distance, first with the left hand and then the right. We really struggled to collect enough beanbags to go around because they were supposed to have 10 bags for each child and on a Tuesday and Thursday they sometimes used them outside for PE.

As usual, I knew by now that things would not go as planned. When they started it was horrendous as their hands went all over and they flapped and flipped. This is what happens when one part of the body moves, the whole flipping ~ flapping body moves. The beanbags were all over, in the kitchen area, the PE boxes, the corridor, in your eye, up your nose, on your head and Norman had lost two altogether. It was like someone who was not concentrating pointing a loaded gun at you with their hand on the trigger: you had to duck a lot! I only realised where Norman's beanbags had gone two weeks later when I saw a teacher discussing something yellow and red on top of the lights in the hall. OOOPS!

If the children stood sideways they couldn't balance nor had any sense of direction. The children were taught to stand completely straight in front of their target (the hoop) and push forward with the hand with the beanbag in and let go.

They also had to hold the beanbag with the whole hand and not fling it while holding with their fingers. At first they struggled because they had a weakness in their arms and hands and had no direction. But eventually they rarely missed as they got stronger and their balance and direction improved.

All the time I was recording in the dinner time, or when I had a spare minute, how they were progressing. It also helped me understand their weaknesses and which new exercises to introduce.

They were all jumping and hopping with very little flapping ("associated movements" ~ the proper name in the books). They could walk along the line without walking on their own feet or flapping and they didn't wobble either. They could all turn the skipping rope completely full circle without whipping which showed their arms and hands were stronger.

Every time I asked them to do a new exercise I asked a child from another class secretly to show me how they could do it. It is quite heartbreaking when you see a co-ordinated child do an exercise and then a child with difficulties struggle.

I was beginning to understand more the importance of the children being able to access both sides of the brain. I decided to try and get the children to use a skateboard to help them strengthen their upper body, which in turn would help them with their left and right laterality (the proper word for both sides of the brain working together) and also their balance and direction.

The only problem was, we didn't have any skateboards and had to borrow four. Two children brought them but argued about sharing, and the other two had to go back to older brothers at the weekend. We unfortunately were never consistent in getting all the equipment at one time in those first months of setting up.

Again, the first time they tried this exercise was a disaster. As I gave the instructions for them to line up, the boys, of course, immediately demonstrated their skills as experienced world champions by trying to stand up on the skateboards and glide across the hall (to impress the girls). I checked for broken limbs as I untangled them and sent them back to the end of the hall. They then argued for at least 10 minutes about who was going first and sharing.

After World War Three and death threats, I asked them to lie on their tummies and walk with their hands left and then right. I attempted to show them how it was done but my body seemed to cascade over the sides and I mentioned that my "bum was too big".

If you mention anything to do with bodies or bodily functions to children, you lose it completely, and they all laughed and cheered as they tried to help me up elegantly. The Head Teacher walked past. He poked his head around the hall curtains saying, "Remember, have fun but be firm." It's a good job he didn't see me on the skateboard!

As I said, "Go," they all set off. Norman ran over Katie's finger, she rolled off and James then ran over her hair, which got stuck in the wheels. Amy was like a bat out of hell as she head-butted the apparatus. Maisy was the only one doing it correctly, although very slowly and with a slight twist to the right, but with grace. The others fell off sideways; some used both hands at the same time instead of left then right. They also had an obvious weakness in their hands and upper body. Most struggled to pull themselves forward with their hands and one even trembled.

One child on a later programme became very distressed at this exercise. A lot of children do get really upset at the realisation of how weak they are in some exercises and how difficult it is. They also get very tired very easily.

I know now that when children use skateboards, you have to be even more conscious of health and safety. The first time they used skateboards they had followed on from the throwing beanbags. Running over a child's bare feet with a skateboard isn't clever so it is a good idea to make this an incentive to put shoes on quickly. It also helps having a good distance between each child and allow two to go at once.

It was easier for children go forwards and backwards at my side with the most challenging ones within reaching distance next to me either side. I tie a rope to the apparatus at the other side of the room, and pull the rope tight. The children have to long sit with feet pointing forwards and pull themselves to the other side. At first the children sat down and automatically turned their hands downwards, like when Jack wrote, as though he was going to stab someone. They might also fall off, and go off to one side.

Eventually, if you keep showing them how to hold it properly with their hands upright, the children learn to automatically hold their hands up. They don't fall off and they go as "straight as a bullet", as Norman would always say.

As I was always monitoring them, I was conscious that when they did anything they kept on going until they fell or, if they headed for anything, they didn't know when to stop. They couldn't judge the distance.

This is, as the books would say, a spatial skill which involves the perception of space and distance.

I had read almost seven books, and hadn't understood most of the jargon, but I had decided to try an exercise with hoops which was supposed to help with this and also eye-foot co-ordination.

Again I shouted, "1, 2, 3!" and they all came to me and stopped. "Line up here."

I positioned eight hoops in a row with enough distance in between to enable them to jump.

Starting at the front I showed them what to do: it wasn't elegant but they always enjoyed my attempts to show them. I was beginning to worry as I seemed at times to be worse than some of them. I had convinced others that I had begun to show them really badly to make them feel better, to entertain them and make them laugh; well that's my story!

Norman started the procedure and jumped once and, just as expected, kept going until he fell. None of them could judge the distance to jump and they all bent their backs, unable to stand up straight.

They also either fell on top of each other, got the hoops wrapped or stuck to their feet or didn't start at the right time. Guess what? Yes, it was chaos.

The children were then instructed to go as directed "in-out, in-out" until the end and then start again for three times.

Eventually, after a week, they stood with their heads up, only some still tiptoeing, only some still flapping, and in perfect time (well working towards). I never aimed for perfect.

I came into school as usual at the beginning of week five. One of the Mums of a child on the programme had stopped me on the way in and asked me if they could come and watch me with another Mum. The school's policy had always been access to parents at all times to our exercise programme so I was quite happy for her to come and see the children. This particular Mum had been to watch her child at the very beginning of the programme (the first week) so had seen the chaos and difficulties that her child was having. I must admit I had assured her that everything would be fine, but at that time I'm sure she was able to sense my panic. She looked tearful, as I reassured her that everything would be fine as she left the hall that day.

I went to collect the children, only to be told that Norman had already been and taken them. I rushed up the corridor to the hall and pulled back the curtain. There were all the children lined up waiting to do their exercises. Their shoes and socks were neatly placed in pairs on the bench.

"Have you done this for them?" I said to the Mums who were sitting on the other side of the hall.

"No, the children have got undressed and are waiting for you."

I was stunned as Norman started the exercises; they jumped, they hopped, they walked the line, they jumped the hoops and they skipped. They quietly got out the beanbags and put them in piles and then threw them into the hoops. I just went along with the organised programme in a trance.

They then put everything away and proceeded with the skateboards.

When they had finished, they went over to the benches and put their shoes and socks on. Those who finished first helped the other slower ones dress. When they finished they said "Goodbye" with a smile and went back to their classes.

I turned to the two Mums and looked at them, they were grinning.

"I was only saying to Norman's Mum how quiet it was since the last time. Wasn't it awful? Aren't they brilliant? Our Norman has completely calmed down at home and his teacher has said he's doing brilliant in class. His Dad, who wasn't happy at all when you said our Norman had difficulties, has built him a pole to walk along at the bottom of the garden and he can waltz across that like a gymnast. He's started playing football with his Dad, so he's well pleased."

"And our George, bless him, went to the pictures for the first time last week and sat all the way through. He's even started bringing books home and his teacher says he has gone up two stages."

"And James's Mum says, James could never swim and he's started using his arms at the right time and he's so confident now like our Norman, he actually likes coming to school which he hated."

They both went along the hall and out of the school.

As I walked back to class I was bursting with pride and all morning I told everyone possible how they had put their shoes on and how brilliant they were.

That dinner time I went to write down their progress. Instead of writing 'W/T' for working towards or 'A' for achieved in the boxes I wrote 'M' for miracle.

6. Resources

In most schools, money is not easily available and I was always struggling to get the resources together to enable our group to work properly. With the approval of our SENCO I tried various avenues for funding and received a letter of support from our local education authority giving us names of charities and funding we could apply to. In between the weeks we were doing the programmes I had applied to a local charity and they telephoned me and arranged a meeting.

We were to be interviewed by a lady and I was very excited on the day of her arrival at the prospect of getting some much needed money. But I should have known by then that it wasn't going to be easy. I started laughing when I was given pages of paperwork for the children to fill in.

She explained that the children needed to write in detail about the exercise programme and the reason they were applying for funding. This was probably easy if they were A level students applying for funding to enable them to climb Mount Everest and conquer inner fears and find their inner strengths.

We were talking children who were just asking to read, write and walk in a straight line without falling over. I explained to her the children's difficulties and, even though we were asking for money for an exercise programme, here were children that struggled with their writing. I explained motor skills problems (dyspraxia) as simply as I could and she realised that she would have to rethink her way of applying in a different way.

She came up with the idea of videotaping the children. She would ask the children questions and they would give their answers on camera.

A date was organised and letters went out to parents to enable us to video the children. Parents were very supportive and thought it was a brilliant idea that the children would have their own equipment and would have a sense of importance.

The children arrived that morning all looking their best; I was very proud.

We started off with her introducing the programme. I then demonstrated the exercise and the children showed what they could do. The only problem was, the children were doing the exercises perfectly and I was the one tripping and falling like an idiot, as I was so nervous.

We finished filming the children going through the exercises and sat the children in a line to introduce themselves.

"Would you like to say your names?" she asked the children, very professionally.

"I'm Amy…" "I'm James…" "I'm Katie…"

"What's my name Miss?"

Katie whacked Norman and Norman whacked her back.

"Norman," Katie whispered.

"Oh! Yes, Norman."

"My name is George…"

"I'm Maisy and I'm very pleased to meet you and of course the people who are going to give us money."

She smiled into the camera sideways, showing her teeth.

Our interviewer then asked the children why they came and Maisy, like a star, didn't let us down. As the other children looked on stunned, she looked into the camera and gave her speech about her difficulties and how her neural pathways were being sorted out and her writing had improved and the benefits of exercising.

She then asked the children if they were to receive some money what they would buy. Well that was it then, they just didn't stop.

"Well, I would buy loads of chocolate and a new Barbie."

"I would go to Disney on holiday."

All the time I was looking at them behind the camera and gesticulating to them, "Skateboards, beanbags, hoops."

The camera kept rolling on and I could see her amusement as they carried on with their Christmas lists.

She looked even more amused as we all sat down and played the video back so the children could see. To say we had filmed a comedy sketch was putting it mildly but she looked pleased as she packed up and went.

I received a telephone call weeks later but I wasn't getting my hopes up as to the outcome. However, we were given £400 to spend on resources as the funding panel thought we were great. I was told that our presentation was natural and one of the best they had ever seen.

One of the panel members had recognised me as she had gone to school with me. I'm sure she must have commented on my co-ordination ability and my teaching skills.

I have watched the video on occasions when I have felt depressed and wondered if I could maybe sell it to people for entertainment purposes!

7.   The End... but just the beginning

The final week came and my little heroes had been brilliant; they could do all the exercises without any problems. I had been inundated with reports from parents and class teachers to say how their children had progressed. One teacher admitted that she had been unsure whether we could make a difference, but had seen the progress the children had made over the weeks and was impressed with the results.

On Wednesday I collected all the children together and handed them a piece of plain white paper. As they all took one, I explained to them that I would like them all to write something for me, anything they wanted, just so I could see if the exercises had made a difference with their handwriting. Usually, they would have all gone, "UGHH! Miss," and complained loudly and tried to avoid this task (apart from Amy WH Smith) but they all ran and found a corner in the hall to write something down.

Norman and George had indeed changed the most and, with both of them in my class, I was able to witness and monitor their progress every day. In particular, Norman had completely calmed down and showed no signs of unusual high motor activity for a boy of his age. Their concentration had improved dramatically and they had both become part of the class. At carpet time especially, you immediately noticed how their hands went straight up to answer questions, which showed that their processing had increased speed.

Norman showed me the letter he had written about his holiday and his sister. Instead of a long continuous snake of letters it now had spaces in between each whole recognisable word.

When George had given me his work at the beginning of the programme it had taken him 20 minutes to draw a smiley face and another 30 minutes to write three different letters of various sizes. George wrote me the most beautiful letter in about 10 minutes. It wasn't perfect, it had some letters that were upside down but I could understand it completely. It had spaces and it said how he was going to live by the seaside and he would miss me and he was upset. "Love George."

Our SENCO passed the hall and I asked her to take a look at George's work. I was trying not to break down in floods of tears because of my pride as she stood by my side. "Look at this letter George has written for me, isn't it wonderful?"

"This is brilliant George, you have never done this, someone else must have done it," she said.

"No Miss, it was me, I've done it myself," he said looking up at us beaming.

We both stood like proud parents at that moment; I felt overwhelmed.

Maisy showed me the full page of work she had done about "happiness" and it was if she had unlocked it all from inside herself. She wrote how cuddling her Mummy made her happy and her Dad tickling her and her sister and chocolate and on and on. Maisy was so happy I thought she was going to explode.

They all showed me their work and it was fantastic, they had achieved everything and more.

On the last day we did the exercises and we all sat down and talked about the past weeks. They all looked genuinely upset when I confessed that they wouldn't be coming anymore. They all hugged me, and I knew I was going to miss being part of their day.

Maisy and Amy asked to show me something they had been practising and, before I knew it, they were upside down standing on their heads saying, "How's that for balancing Mrs Smith?"

If you had asked me before they were on the programme if I thought it was possible for them to do headstands I would have become hysterical.

Katie and Amy still come to the care club I work in after school. Amy doesn't draw as much and plays outside every day (weather permitting) with all the other children. Her Mum told me she had to put shorts under her dresses as she was always doing handstands. It was getting embarrassing in the Co-op as she showed off her new ability and knickers!

Katie's Mum is always coming in to tell us that she won't be coming as another friend has invited her to tea. Katie has lots of friends now and she runs around a lot, she never stands still like she used to.

James progressed in class slowly and his only complaint now about school is the dinners. James loves coming to school for the first time ever and he runs around like a bullet at playtime with all his friends.

At Christmas I watched three girls on stage performing a dance with their class. Last year they fell off like skittles until they went on the programme. This year with co-ordination, timing and grace, Maisy and her friends danced like real prima ballerinas.

8.   Many children later

That was over five years ago, although it seems a lifetime away. The characters are made up of a mixture of children and people I have encountered over the years and the difficulties children struggled with and how they overcame them.

The children on the programme I wrote about were the first six of over 80 children I have worked with in over five years. This year I start with another 10.

I am almost certain that all of the children would have stayed on the Special Needs Register and would have made little progress. The few children that have stayed on are only on because they need to catch up with their hand writing/reading at School Action. They would no longer climb up the Special Needs Register for their learning/behaviour as before.

Maisy does exist and had very real difficulties but her parents are so pleased with her progress that they were quite happy to let other people celebrate in her success by reading about her. Maisy was diagnosed as having dyspraxia, dyslexia and dyscalculia, which meant that she was definitely a candidate to be put on the Special Needs Register. Maisy's parents hired a tutor for her dyslexia and were advised to contact a centre for dyspraxia and read Madeleine Portwood's book, to exercise at home.

For children to exercise at home can be a mammoth task as homework itself for most children is an inconvenience. As with Mrs Smith, implementing a programme and still having the support from school was difficult. Ideally, children need other children to be part of a team and in school this works the best, but something is better than nothing.

Maisy was definitely a star who shone very brightly and has had phenomenal success because she was determined to overcome her difficulties. She will be a prima ballerina one day.

Numerous books that I have read about dyspraxia claim that your child "Will be assessed by an Occupational Therapist and they will draw up an appropriate plan. This plan may include individual or group therapy session." The truth is (because I was told by an Occupational Therapist), dyspraxia is regarded as the lowest priority for funding and you will be given a booklet on dyspraxia and the OT will say "Good luck."

A Physiotherapist in one book tells you that they will advise you to "ensure your child is included in PE as much as possible". Every school encourages all children to be included in PE but this doesn't solve the problem. As with Jack, it lowers their self-esteem and they usually fail miserably and, again like Jack, it is akin to rubbing a sore until it bleeds.

Therapists may advise on helping a child to master dressing, tying shoe laces and advise non-slip mats for eating, but this just deals with the symptoms and not the illness itself.

I was informed that the school I work in is above average with children with motor skills difficulties, or maybe our school has the ability to screen children and deal with the difficulties. At a workshop held at our school to enable us to share our programme with other professionals a lady put her hand up and said, "I'm just here out of curiosity really, we haven't any children with any motor skills difficulties in our school." As she left she admitted that in her mind she could see children with varying difficulties in her school.

The exercises I use now are mainly taken from the Madeleine Portwood book, although I have tried (and used) many more from other books on my quest over the years to overcome motor skills difficulties.

You need to start programmes early, before difficulties become embedded and children get into the trap where they are years behind. As with Jack, he had learnt avoidance strategies of bad behaviour.

If you observe children in Nursery and Reception, allowing for immaturity of motor skills (because children progress at different levels), you can become aware of any early weaknesses.

With dyspraxia, the left and right side of the brain are not working together. Children are unable to progress past the CVC stage because both sides of the brain need to work together to enable children to blend and make whole words. Children seem fine in Reception until they reach Year 1 and this is when I have seen the difficulties start leading up to Year 2.

If a child is at the early teaching stage and they have their motor skills difficulties corrected at the same time, they may need only a few months of support instead of years.

I was once told, "There is no research to prove that exercises work, if exercises had not been used these children may have progressed eventually."

As a support assistant and mother of a child who struggled with dyslexia (only to realise when I started these programmes that he really had dyspraxia), I know this is incorrect.

Children I have worked with following years of support using different strategies to enable them to progress, make little or no progress and lose years of learning.

I look back at children that I have supported for years and now realise that they had those telltale signs I am now aware of. Because of ignorance you just keep trying different strategies.

It was suggested by a professional that the only way to confirm this theory to see if it is correct is by monitoring a group of children in a controlled test. Half of the children would be on the programme and the other half would not (but with the same teaching methods) and see who progressed. After five years of seeing children overcome their difficulties following the programme I would never withdraw support from a child just to see if their theory was right. With the results I have seen in children, I know it works.

Following the programme, which "kick starts their brain," they suddenly progress and make significant improvements in their learning.

As special needs children are being integrated into mainstream schools, you feel that it is only right that you give the best support you can. Support assistants are becoming experts in special needs, unlike when we first started our jobs and the advert said "There is a vacancy for a kind, caring individual to look after a child with learning difficulties."

We all started off learning to photocopy and laminate. Many years down the line you are an expert in ADHD, autism/Asperger's, cerebral palsy, dyslexia, dyspraxia, and dyscalculia, learning/ behaviour difficulties and many other problems.

Because you go on many courses, and work with so many different children, you notice a similarity of behaviours and symptoms or, as the experts would say, "under the same umbrella".

I began to understand that because neural pathways are weakened in children with dyspraxia, this enabled associated behaviours to be released in these children.

Imagine

Imagine supporting a child with significant learning difficulties along with being diagnosed with autism/Asperger's and the targets set are to make progress with reading and writing. Even though every strategy was tried over years, this child failed to progress at an acceptable rate.

When the child is screened, obvious motor skills weaknesses are evident. The child is put on the programme and starts making remarkable progress in reading and writing and manages most of the exercises.

Again, the quality of teaching never altered but the programme allows that "kick start" and the child is able to progress.

Imagine a child who has started school and fights all the time at home and school. Professionals investigate and support this child as thought to be in the autistic spectrum. This child is able to be controlled with good behaviour management and very rarely lashes out in class. As soon as this child is allowed outside at playtime the aggression starts. When brought inside and spoken to, this child seems to repeat or not understand the reason for being brought into school as a consequence.

The child was observed and it was noticed that, instead of communicating quickly to react, the child hit other children.

When screened this child had significant (severe) motor skills difficulties and was put on the programme.

This child was unable to project from the floor to jump or move, had no balance, direction, judgement of distance and tracking. His processing was extremely poor, which explained the delay in responding quickly in situations at playtime.

Following six months of exercises his parents have noticed a significant difference. This child has very few episodes of aggression at home. He rarely strikes out at school but when this does happen, is able to explain why, apologise and accept the consequences. This child is now a pleasure to have in class and be part of his school. This child now processes quickly, has no weaknesses in direction, distance, balance, tracking and his behaviour is no longer a problem.

Children may be diagnosed as having autism/Asperger's and also have associated behaviours linking to motor skills difficulties. Isn't it better to eliminate these difficulties instead of living with them because it is part of the problem and surely anyone would rather just have mild autism/Asperger's, because that is quite enough, thank you?

To talk to a child who makes no eye contact, has no social interaction, talks about the same thing (obsessive) likes routines and they also seem to be in a world of their own. You immediately start putting a child under that multi-coloured umbrella, thinking autism or along that spectrum.

If you are a dyspraxic child and you have to make eye contact, this means you have to process more information than you need to. You have to look at their mouth, hear what they say and work out body language. In Jack's case you know that you are going to invariably get into trouble if your TA doesn't understand your difficulties.

As with Jack, playing is difficult. You cannot run at the same pace, you fall, you can't process games quickly enough, you want to socially interact but you just give up.

A routine is safe and information has already been processed and this can appear as obsessive.

Once children have been on the programme, they are able to process information as their pathways are now strengthened. They make more eye contact, they now have balance, direction and judgement of distance. They run faster with confidence around the playground like everyone else. Suddenly, they begin to interact and gain friends.

They no longer daydream and again, because pathways are strengthened, they process more quickly and become part of the class.

Supporting children with special needs over the years means that you know when a child has truly got ADHD or not. When the Ritalin wears off and a pair of scissors flies past your head, you know the difference between that and high motor activity (another associated behaviour).

Jack felt dizzy when he sat down and the only relief he got was to move around in class. As with many of the children, once they have their balance corrected, this constant movement and restlessness subsides.

To staff who are untrained and have no understanding of dyspraxic children, you could indeed mistake these similar behaviours and put a child in this spectrum of ADHD.

With all of the children who showed very high motor activity, this was the area that probably changed the most rapidly. I was never aware of when children "calmed down", it just crept up and you realised the noise level and moving around constantly wasn't there.

Dyspraxic children always have varying degrees of dyslexia at the beginning of the programme and this is one of the main reasons the children are chosen because of an educational response.

Handwriting samples before and after show whether children make significant progress and which areas need addressing following the programmes.

Most of the children who have been on the programme still had underlying difficulties that needed to be addressed, especially with literacy, because they were so many years behind.

I started to understand how the whole system of learning can be altered if only one area of the body is affected.

I understood that we have four modalities for reading and spelling/writing: visual (eyes), auditory (ears), oral kinesthetic, (mouth) and manual (hands). Or looking, listening, speaking and writing.

When you read a word, you look at the letters in a word, link to the remembered sound and pronounce the word; this takes three modalities.

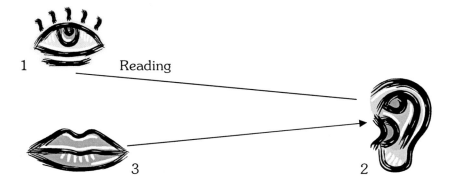

When spelling a child hears the sounds in the word, repeats them and produces a hand movement to make the correct shape for the letters and then a word. They will then check visually that the word is correct using four modalities. If only one modality was impaired, this would have an effect on learning.

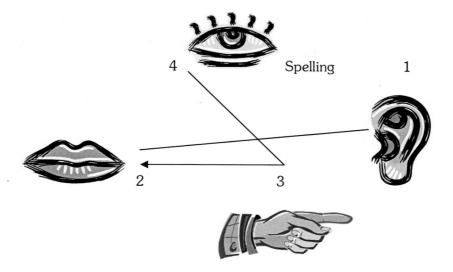

Most of the children I have worked with are able readers: it was difficult to understand how a child could read well but be struggling to write and spell. I now understand that if a child only has to have three modalities for reading then this was simple for them because they could read easily without the writing (manual) modality.

One child I worked with was unable to read because of his tracking (visual), which was the missing piece.

Another child was unable to read because of his auditory (ears). He had overcome his manual (hands) and his oral kinesthetic (speech) was fine. His tracking (visual) was no longer a problem as he was seeing an optometrist for visual training, but still failed to progress. This left his auditory (ears). I realised that he was unable to retain a sound unless you segmented or blended each phoneme up and said it first, it would then trigger a word. The child is learning the sounds consistently every day with a dyslexic programme and is now progressing. The child was diagnosed by an Educational Psychologist as having auditory dyslexia.

If a child has the missing modalities for spelling (eyes, hands or speech) and for writing (eyes or hands) this is when all the difficulties start as they are all needed to write and spell.

Some children may also have short term memory and, as mentioned, auditory (ears) difficulties would therefore find linking and retaining the remembered sound difficult (auditory dyslexia).

Seeing a child eight years old who had been diagnosed with verbal dyspraxia but was then screened and found to have significant motor skills difficulties (dyspraxia), you can imagine the frustration this child would have.

This child's tracking (eyes) auditory (ears) were fine. But his manual (motors) and speech (mouth) were the problem.

Imagine working with this child with these weaknesses and seeing them overcome all of the motor skills difficulties. At the beginning of the programme the child was on a Reception level reading scheme. In six months this child is now on stage 6 level reading. The only difficulties the child has now are pronouncing a few letters incorrectly when speaking, otherwise speech (modality) is understandable and the child never stops talking.

Imagine a child with speech and language difficulties or (SLD) who has undertaken therapy for speech problems before entering school. The child makes very slow progress with their education and is screened for motor skills difficulties. Significant weaknesses are found and the child is put on a programme of exercises.

Questions are asked.

Why are children with speech problems not automatically screened for motor skills difficulties?

What if this child had continued in a school that didn't screen or have a programme of exercises to support this child?

Is speech a more obvious sign of difficulty?

Should special SLD schools automatically screen and implement an exercise programme?

As well as being on a programme which has supported your child in overcoming difficulties in processing, direction, distance and balance, your child may still require speech therapy, visual training and dyslexic tutoring.

Working with over 80 children in five years I saw only two children who needed an optometrist for vision training and three who saw tutors for dyslexia. These children were on the programme when they were older and had fallen two years or more behind.

Socially, children who have been on the programme change the most dramatically because of the increased amounts of confidence with achieving and improvement with processing.

They have been on a programme of motor skills that is extremely difficult and have been able to see their achievements. Children learn how to play, having previously felt rejected through lack of interaction.

Children are now able to hold a conversation instead of repeating information that had been processed over and over again because it was quick (safe).

Because their concentration is improved, children play for longer without wandering off.

Before (as with Jack), they would forget what they were playing, lose concentration and wander off or again fail to hold their concentration for long. No one wants to play with a forgetful, daydreaming, clumsy and grumpy child; other children tend to avoid you.

Children who struggled with fine motor skills start playing with other children at board games and construction. Before, they would knock toys over or take too long to make things.   The thing you notice the most is the speed at which children run around at playtime: instead of being put in the accident book for falling over they are now put in for hitting things at a great speed.

9.   The Programme

The exercises to be used in this programme were taken from various books but were mainly chosen and used for their impact.

Some schools hold motor skills summer clubs for children and the majority of their exercise programmes last for six weeks. Most of the books you read recommend the same period of time and, for the majority of children with minor weaknesses, this is fine. Through experience, a consistent daily exercise programme that deals with all the weaknesses at once has the only lasting effect.

You need a programme that will maintain and strengthen the neural pathways long enough for children to overcome difficulties for good.

Children that had accessed the programme for just six weeks started showing the same difficulties as before. This usually showed up with slow processing in that the children started to "daydream" again. This is not easy if you are a school just starting a programme and you have a lot of children with difficulties.

Programmes should continue for as long as children need it and, as every child's difficulties vary in severity, some children have been on for as long as two years. Any weaknesses left were then highlighted and corrected with specific exercises.

Experts recommend that children should be screened no younger than seven years old, allowing for immaturities in motor skills. The truth is that at this age it is too late and associated behaviours/learning difficulties are escalating and becoming embedded. Children will have already lost the chance to maximise their potential. Because of this they move steadily up the Special Needs Register.

I see children in Nursery and Reception struggling at this age and you could leave these children for the recommended years. But through experience, these children very rarely progress if they have obvious motor skills/learning difficulties. I know because my job was to support these children later in class.

Children will be taken to the doctors by emotional parents as dyspraxia is a medical condition, and passed on to an Occupational Therapist. The OT will diagnose dyspraxia after every strategy and support in school has been exhausted. Parents will be advised and given a booklet with exercises in and told "Good luck" and yes, I have evidence to support this from professionals and parents.

I was very lucky in that, following the programme in the morning, I was also supporting children in class and I was then able to see the difficulties in all areas, especially literacy.

As children's bodies became balanced with the exercises so did their brains and they started to write whole words and leave spaces. They also overcame their high motor activity (or were able to sit and do their work without using avoidance strategies). As their neural pathways strengthened, so did their processing, and they began to listen, followed instructions, kept up with work and behaviour wasn't a problem.

Balance, perceptual, spatial awareness and tracking were all seen to improve. New friendships were made and, most importantly, they smiled as self-confidence grew.

In our school, through early intervention, we have children in Reception/Year 1 on a programme. We are now working at the same time on their phonemic awareness so that the gap between themselves and their peers won't widen too dramatically.

I wish that every school could screen and produce an exercise programme because how many more children will have to wait to be diagnosed with dyspraxia/dyslexia by experts and allowed to struggle? I now realise that many more children are being diagnosed with dyslexia when the root cause was dyspraxia, as my son was.

Ideally, all children would be doing a set of exercises every morning as part of the National Curriculum. This would mean overcoming any motor skills difficulties which impact on learning.

Before you start a programme you must have an understanding of the children you are working with. These children may have had years of low self-esteem due to failure in one or more areas of school life. Whether it is something as simple as not being able to throw a ball in PE or having every problem there is, is possible.

The first job is to make children feel as though every achievement they make is worth something, however small.

On a course I attended a child psychologist once asked the students how many times they said something good to a child. I admitted that I never did. We were asked to say something complimentary at least 50 times a day to a child and see how it made us feel. It felt awkward at first but after a while you can see the look of pleasure from a child when you just say something as simple as them having nice hair. As an adult, I know if someone compliments me in any way it makes me feel wonderful (also, at my age, grateful).

Patience is another valuable asset to have if you want to succeed as these children will sometimes take weeks and months to progress. For most staff in schools this is second nature when working with children. But like me ignorance went with frustration. I at least knew that these children would progress eventually, unlike before when every resource had been exhausted.

Instructions must be very simple and uncomplicated as processing is delayed. If you are supporting children with speech and language difficulties (verbal dyspraxia) this is especially important.

Staff must always be aware that children must be monitored at all times because you may have children with no direction, balance or co-ordination, delayed processing (they don't seem to listen) and high motor activity.

In many books about dyspraxia they tell you about how an infant will reach for an object in a cot and messages will go to all four limbs and unnecessary neural pathways are used. Over months, as a child grows and reinforces the appropriate neural pathways, the unnecessary pathways disappear and a child will make a rapid response. Dyspraxic children do not eliminate the unnecessary pathways and this is when the problems start.

I explain to children that it is a bit like going along a main road from where you live to a town. You are supposed to go straight along the road without stopping but dyspraxic children go the long way around and stop at villages and shops before they get to town and that is why it takes a long time to follow instructions (process). In some children they stop off at Grandma's and have a cup of tea!

Exercise 1 ~ To jump forwards 5 metres between two lines, three times.

This is the first exercise to wake the body up and get messages to only two parts of the body. It is the most difficult at first because all the messages to move are going to every part of the body (as with the neural pathways) and everything moves. Children may/will flap their hands, stick out their tongues, bend forwards and keep going until they fall. Children may have a lower body weakness and find it difficult to project from the floor and some will tiptoe. These are called associated movements and in most books it advises you to stop the exercises once associated movements disappear.

I have found that children need to carry on with this exercise to enable the whole body and neural pathways to strengthen.

It helps if children hold beanbags in their hands to help them keep their hands down.

Children will eventually project easily from the floor to at least three inches with both feet together and land on their heels.

Associated movements will go and children will jump with their hands down loosely by their sides. They will be able to jump with their backs straight and keep moving forwards without falling. Lower body strength is increased, together with direction and judgement.

Exercise 2 ~ To hop on the left/right foot for 5 metres between two lines, three times.

Children will again show all the associated movements as with jumping feet together. Most children will show a weak side and, as you need both sides of the brain working together, it is important to get this imbalance corrected. This also aims to get messages to only one part of the body.

Everyone has a weak side usually but MSD children show a specific weakness.

When hopping, children may fall forward and go sideways on the weak side or fall down.

Some children will need lifting with one hand under their arm to enable them to project off the floor, to get the rhythm of jumping and to allow a child to gain strength.

This programme was used with a child with cerebral palsy who had a weak left side. After six months of lifting by myself and another child, and determination, this child hopped 40 times around the hall independently. This child's handwriting improved considerably, self-esteem and confidence grew. Parents and the Occupational Therapist were delighted as they had found it was very difficult to follow an exercise programme at home and it allowed this child to work with other children as a team.

Children will eventually project from the floor without any associated movements, hop with no weaknesses from either side, bodies will be upright and lower body strength, balance, direction and judgement of distance will be improved.

Exercise 3 ~ To walk along a 5 metre measured line on the floor, heel to toe.

To avoid wasting time it is a good idea to have the children doing this on the way back from jumping. This enables them to get their breath back/calm down and also keep at a reasonable distance apart. This will avoid congestion when lining up and the children getting distracted. You are also able to stand in the middle of the lines and monitor both exercises and keep in control.

Children will have associated movements and will at first walk on their own toes. They will also try and walk sideways, fall over and their backs will be arched forward.

Children will eventually have no associated movements, will not fall over, backs will be straight and they will walk heel to toe.

This will help children with their balance, direction, judgement of distance, eye-foot co-ordination and lower body strength.

Following this exercise you can then take children to a higher level of achievement by using a bench turned up so that the children can walk along a two inch wide beam.

This enables the children to really test their balance and the ultimate challenge is to be able to stand on one leg on the bench, singing a nursery rhyme, a poem or just talking. If a child can concentrate on singing etc. (learning in class) and not think about their balance, this is the ultimate achievement.

This was certainly true for Jack, who was unable to learn because he was too busy trying to keep his balance.

I always try and imagine myself in a room being a student and listening to a tutor when there is an earthquake happening. Would you listen to a lecturer speaking and concentrate on what they were saying or try and keep safe and hold on to your desk?

The next level is to use the benches and trellises to build an obstacle course which allows the children to climb up high and balance. This not only challenges the children but builds up self-esteem. The children can see how they have overcome fears and can achieve like everyone else. This, like the skateboards, is probably the most favourite exercise.

***Exercise 4 ~ To jump in and out of 15 hoops placed
on the floor with spaces in between at a regular pace.***

This exercise was chosen as I had noticed children had difficulty
with judging distance and direction or, as experts would say,
difficulty with perceptual development.

This is when a child has static balance (the ability to maintain a
position when standing) or dynamic balance the ability to maintain
a position while the body is moving)

Spatial awareness is the understanding of the external space
surrounding a person and the ability to move in and out through
that space. This, as I understand it, is when you know there is a
chair behind you and judging the distance it would take for you to
sit your bottom on it, or knowing where a piece of furniture is and
avoiding it.

Body and directional awareness is the ability to understand how to
produce various movements and the body's potential in
movement. Directionality is the understanding of up and down
and left and right.

I saw this in a classroom as children who would fall off a
chair/table or try and go through a door and bump into the frame
and who had no concept of what their body was doing.

Some parents have children's eyes tested and, of course, their
focus is never a problem.

To someone who has no understanding of this problem (myself
included in the past), this is a child acting carelessly or messing
about.

When children first attempt this exercise they keep jumping with their backs arched until they fall. They struggle to keep at a correct pace of instructions (in-out-in-out) and they may tiptoe.

Children eventually jump with their backs straight with no associated movements and are able to judge the distance between each hoop. As children's processing is increased they keep up with the correct pace and can jump in-out-in-out without breaking the flow. Children will also jump with both feet together instead of tiptoeing. If a child has slow processing you can see the delay in following the instructions and, over weeks, you can see the delay decreasing. If asked to stop/go they will immediately.

An extension of this is to play traffic lights where children are given tasks to do at given colours for instructions. This not only helps with developing processing skills but can be used for perceptual difficulties. Children can be asked to move and hold a position or keep a position while moving. For spatial awareness children learn how to move without bumping into anyone, which is essential in any playground.

Exercise 5 ~ To turn a skipping rope with a partner 20 times with the left/right arm turning 360°.

When children first attempt this they whip from side to side with associated movements of the hand not holding the skipping rope. They tend to use their elbow to turn and may manage only a few turns before they lose control. They may also shake their head from side to side until they are dizzy.

Children need this weakness and control corrected to enable them to strengthen their weakened upper body. It strengthens their shoulders, arms, wrists and hands, and their power to write (fine motor control) and throw/catch balls etc.

Over weeks they are able to turn the rope a full 360° large circle where hands are extended upward and then down with no associated movements. They do not break the pace and can achieve 20 plus turns without shaking their heads.

Exercise 6 ~ To throw a beanbag from the left hand to the right hand in an arc with eyes focussed on the beanbag, 20 times.

This is one of the most difficult and necessary exercises to make an impact in children's learning.

Sight is the ability to see and the eye's responses to light shining into it. This exercise supports children who at the beginning are unable to track (see visual problems) on the beanbag and also have a weakness in their hand.

Some children find it difficult to pass the beanbag over (cross the midline) and will pass the beanbag over their chests and cross hands, instead of throwing back and forwards in the air. As the body grows, interweaving of the opposite sides through movement naturally occurs during such activities as crawling, walking and running.

Research has shown that the majority of dyspraxic children bottom shuffle, pushing forward all the limbs, or they pull themselves up using two limbs in unison. Children that crawl are stimulating the right and left side of the brain; this enables both sides of the brain to work together.

I have actually seen a child long sitting with a beanbag on the floor to the left side unable to pick the beanbag up with the right hand. Finishing the programme, the child was able to achieve this and throw a beanbag from left to right high into the air with no problems.

Following the programme, children are able to focus on the beanbag in a high arc from left to right. Children who write from the middle of the page to the edge of the book begin writing from the margin, as they are able to cross the midline.

Children increase upper body strength.

When using the Madeleine Portwood screening test I always include throwing a beanbag from left to right, using the beanbag to look for tracking difficulties. I also test for weaknesses crossing the midline with passing the beanbag across the body long sitting.

To check for left/right laterality difficulties I would also ask a child to crawl. This may look simple but I have found that it is very rare that children on the programme can crawl properly.

I have seen children raising up off the floor like a crab and galloping with two hands and two feet. They will start off with left knee ~ right hand ~ left hand ~ right knee and then get completely mixed up. It is a good idea to start with this exercise everyday by doing a lap of the hall to warm up.

To extend this exercise, once tracking is established and to establish left and right laterality, you can also throw the beanbag from the left hand, under the right leg at the front, catch with the right hand, throw with the right hand under the left leg and catch with the left hand.

Another is to throw the beanbag up and clap once, then up and clap twice, then up and clap three times, and so on. Children love this as they really stretch themselves and become competitive ~ but beware of the height of the beanbag when thrown.

Children will be able to move on to throwing balls, beginning with very large ones and then increasing the distance of throwing, catching and eventually minimising the size of the ball.

It is a good idea to always start with a beanbag as they stop where they fall, unlike balls.

Exercise 7 ~ To throw 10 beanbags at a target (hoop or net) with the left/right hand 5 metres away.

At first the children may throw the beanbag with one foot in front and spin to aim. Children must be taught to stand with their feet together, the other hand by their side, look down their arm, push and let go, aiming forwards towards the target.

I was questioned about this as, in PE, children are encouraged to stand with one foot in front. I showed them the balanced way and my ability to hit the target every time without missing and I was never questioned again.

Because of a weakness in their upper body, balance, judgement of distance, direction and hand-eye co-ordination is difficult. The children may also bend forwards.

This exercise helps with sitting to write (balance) and eye/hand co-ordination.

Over weeks the children learn to stand upright, hold their hand by their side (no associated movements), feet together and push forwards, let go of the bean bag and hit the target, or near enough. The upper body and hand-eye co-ordination is also strengthened.

Exercise 8 ~ To long sit on a skateboard and pull forwards with a rope tied 5 metres away.

This exercise was chosen because it was based on balance, direction, spatial awareness, left/right laterality, upper body and fine motor strength.

Children will at first fall to one side (usually the weak side). If you observe, you will notice a child will hold their hands like a dagger instead of cupping inwards (as with Jack when he was writing).

The exercise supports the child to overcome all the above mentioned and, because hands (grip) are strengthened, they begin to turn into the correct position and this in turn helps handwriting.

This activity/exercise is usually done on a Friday as a reward for hard work and also because skateboards need careful monitoring.

This exercise is also voted the favorite and the most envied in school.

Exercise 9 ~ To lie face down on the skateboard and with the hands moving forward in a crawling position.

Children may find this very difficult in moving forwards as it requires a lot of upper body strength, balance, direction and spatial awareness (bumping into others) and left/right laterality. Children may strain to get a grip to pull forwards and will try and pull with both hands (like a swimmer doing a butterfly stroke).

They will eventually be able to use a crawling motion, go in a straight line without bumping into anyone and keep from falling off (balance).

This again is used as a reward but is still necessary and although children don't realise, this is the most strenuous exercise.

Exercise 10 ~ To stand in a space and, starting with the left foot, make a windmill.

Left foot kick out, left foot kick out, left arm up, right arm up, right leg kick out, right leg kick out and back right leg, right leg, right arm, left arm left leg, left leg and around 30 times or more if you have time.

At first children will not keep up as it is using balance, stimulating the left and right hemisphere, spatial awareness and processing. The idea is not to do it too quickly as it not only enables children to follow the instructions but also to help with balance.

It only takes a couple of weeks but this is a brilliant exercise, especially as a brain gym in class. Children like to see how many they can do without making a mistake and love competitions against adults to catch them out.

If you do a hundred of these, as some children have challenged me to on numerous occasions, you can actually feel the benefit (I felt clear headed) and I highly recommend this exercise, especially for hangovers.

I am asked occasionally by teachers, "How do you tell if a child is just not listening when they have been on your programme? Is it because they still cannot process quickly enough or they are pretending?"

I use one exercise just to see how fast children's processing has increased. You can watch them when they are jumping in and out of the hoops as you can actually see a delay in jumping (processing) or you can try this one:

Taking it in turns ask four children to take a musical instrument (triangle, recorder, tambourine and a small shaker) and stand at each corner of the hall. The other children stand in the middle of the room with their eyes closed and head down. You direct with signs the children with the instruments to quietly make a little sound and the children in the middle of the room have to turn to the sound.

It does work and is very useful in finding out who is pulling a fast one (and there is always one).

Most of the exercises deal with fine motor skills difficulties without being that obvious. Holding the beanbags strengthens the grip, as does pulling the rope when exercising with the skateboards. Children pulling themselves forward in a crawling position when lying on a skateboard strengthens the wrists, as does turning the skipping rope.

I have only seen one child who showed a significant weakness with fine motor skills following the programme. To overcome this you can either purchase a programme of exercises for fine motors or, as these can be quite expensive, you can make your own.

Children are asked to transfer a number (50) beads from one container to the next using every finger and thumb in a pincer grip. The beads start off large and eventually go to very small which increases the grip and strength. They are asked to thread beads onto a lace and you can make a shape with holes in and ask a child to thread around. A child I worked with used these exercises every day for at least three months with parents taking it in turns every day. Grandparents even took over in the school holidays but following this the child was able to overcome a severe tremor when writing.

Children's handwriting doesn't always improve immediately as it takes time, but what you notice is the amount children write at first. This will invariably strengthen fine motor skills as they write more and this will also have a positive impact on letter formation. Because children are able to concentrate and balance is corrected, they will then be able to concentrate on learning (punctuation, spacing, imagination, etc.).

That is all the exercises that are used daily in the programme. The routine is never changed to allow for all pathways to be strengthened. The best possible way to overcome motor skills weaknesses are to have a consistent exercise programme that shows to have a specific impact on learning.

Most of the children I have worked with over the years have made significant progress with handwriting. Before and after evidence shows this and some children have astounded me at how quickly they have overcome their difficulties.

This doesn't mean that children are instantly cured just because their motor skills have been corrected. Children will have invariably fallen behind in their learning. They have been "kick-started" and following the programme most of the children I have worked with get a new sense of achievement and increased self-esteem and confidence. This is when the teaching begins. You would never expect a student who was learning to speak a new language to suddenly carry on halfway through their course if they had missed months/years of lessons.

These children may be two years behind their cognitive age and they are no longer in a class doing CVC words. Their class may have progressed to paragraphs and adjectives etc. But, with support, these children do progress unlike before.

Treatment now saves money on ongoing support in the future!

10. After The Programme

Following the programme, most of the children (almost 80) progressed and showed no lasting significant difficulties in school.

Unfortunately, we still had a few children who had weaknesses with their literacy and numeracy even though they had overcome their motor skills difficulties.

Through research I understood that the ability to learn relies on your four modalities. I had addressed the motor skills difficulties so I then looked at the other three areas. At least the children had eliminated one difficulty but to overcome the other modalities you have to understand how they work together as a whole.

There were three children who still didn't make any progress and the question was: Why are they still not able to progress in their reading and writing?

With one of the children (a boy) the programme had corrected all his areas of weaknesses (processing, high motor activity, tracking, gross & fine motor skills) and he no longer showed any associated movements. Unlike the other children, who had all progressed, I was still trying every strategy possible in literacy and numeracy but it was failing. He was stuck and I was well and truly stuck.

We had corrected his manual modality and we had looked at his oral kinesthetic (mouth), his understanding (receptive), and his use (expressive) of language had never been a concern as he was very articulate.

As with most children who struggle with dyspraxia, these children have general/high intelligence and ability but they are unable to "get it out," as one child once told me.

Visual (Eyes)

Whenever there is a problem with children with learning difficulties, you go through the list of eliminating every obstacle.

Children are monitored from birth by the health visitor but I was informed that this year the pre-school eye tests have now been withdrawn because of government cuts. School nurses or health visitors only test for focus and refer children to an optician with other problems such as a squint (lazy eye), diabetes, short/long sight or a family history of eye problems. A general eye test will continue throughout school with the school nurse. All opticians/optometrists would recommend that all children are advised to have an eye test by an optician as one in five children can have an undetected eye problem.

Children's vision can change rapidly as young eyes develop, so eye examinations are important for a child's vision and health care.

Children's experiences over the first few years of life set the stage for their educational and adult lives. Vision is learned and developed through these experiences. It is normally acquired through life experiences. To develop a well-functioning visual process capable of meeting all the demands of life the individual needs to have encountered many development opportunities throughout early life.

The difference between an average athlete and an elite athlete most often is the difference in visual abilities.

Research shows that when a baby makes its first movements to grasp at an object suspended in the line of vision, instinctively all four limbs will thrash around wildly as the child seeks to make contact with the object. Every so often the child will, by chance, be able to

» Fixate on the object

» Extend from the shoulder

» Move the elbow appropriately

» Extend fingers

» Touch the object

Observation of the child shows messages going to all four limbs and this is the result of transmission along unnecessary neural pathways.

If you then put the motor skills difficulties together with the importance of visual training from birth, you can link many children's problems. If you already have a child who is unable to co-ordinate its limbs at the same time, they are going to be unable to develop the necessary visual training required.

Vision training requires developing the visual

» **Focus** ~ the ability to see things clearly at all distances, but being able to shift focus quickly and hold an image clearly without effort.

» **Fixation** ~ the ability to aim and move eyes to the same place at the same time without effort. Eyes staying on target i.e. following a line of print.

» **Fusion** ~ using two eyes at the same time to give depth, 3D perception.

» **Fields** ~ the ability to process information in our periphery which allows us to direct and aim our eyes, process and understand what we are reading.

» **Flexibility** ~ is the ultimate use of all aspects of Focus, Fixation, Fusion, Fields and the integration of the mental processing of reading, comprehension, memory, balance, rhythm, timing directionality, and integration with the other senses.

I had already worked with over 80 children and they all had tracking difficulties when screened.

Focus is tested by a school nurse and all the children had clear vision but their ability to shift focus quickly (following with their eyes/throwing a beanbag from left to right) was a problem for all the children.

Fixation. As most of the children were unable to track a beanbag, this showed in class with the inability to track a line of text when reading or writing or any close work, and in the discomfort you could see in children trying to concentrate on white boards.

Fusion is especially important in a school for children struggling to perceive and judge distance, especially moving around quickly (in the playground), jumping through hoops and throwing in the programme highlighted this problem.

Fields. There was only one child who didn't progress even though all other areas had been addressed.

Following an assessment from an optometrist who was specialised in vision/light therapy, it was found that the child's peripheral vision was significantly reduced. This child had an inability to process any information around him, as it was very minimal. When reading and writing, he could see individual letters but struggled to see or put them into whole words or use information around him as a clue (as needed in reading). Through light therapy and visual training this child started to make progress as his peripheral vision increased.

Learning Problems and Vision

Symptoms

» Poor concentration
» Fatigue with reading or close work
» Short attention span
» Difficulty keeping pace/place when reading
» Continued finger following to keep place
» Slow word to word reading
» Reversals of letters
» Skips, rereads or omits words or whole lines
» Poor handwriting
» Tight grip
» Covers one eye when reading
» Poor co-ordination
» Frustration at close work
» Blurry vision
» Words moving
» Eye strain
» Headaches/dizziness

Of the five senses, vision accounts for 80% of learning. Changing how the visual system functions is changing how the brain processes information. Vision is the ability to use our eyes properly, efficiently and to derive meaning from the result of these actions.

As vision and learning are connected, a vision problem can be mistaken for a learning problem. Seeing is the same as understanding and we need to understand what we see because seeing is one of the most important areas that can have an impact on learning.

I already understood that a child needed to use their motor skills when they are born to have a rapid response to grasp things. The same thing happens to babies when they are born.

When a child is lying in their cot they look up at you.

» They track an object and their eyes stay on track (the same as following a line of print when reading and writing)

» Teaming skills (both eyes working together)

» Binocular vision (both eyes blending the images from both eyes into one image)

» Accommodation (focussing)

» Visual-motor integration (eye hand co-ordination, catching balls etc.)

» Visual perception (memory, perception, directionality)

To enable a child to succeed in all these aspects of sight they must be able to synchronise and co-ordinate their body at the same time to achieve full potential.

Some children with learning difficulties can have specific behaviours of being impulsive, hyperactive and easily distracted. Children can be misdiagnosed as having Attention Deficit Hyperactivity Disorder (ADHD). A vision problem can show the same signs and similarities and children can be labelled with ADHD.

Research has shown that a significant percentage of children with learning difficulties have some type of vision problem. Children diagnosed with ADHD should also be evaluated for "convergence insufficiency" and treated accordingly.

Children who have learning related visual problems can't sustain their close-up work at school and may be misdiagnosed as having ADHD, because children with ADHD can't sustain attention on desk work and schoolwork: same behaviours, same diagnosis.

Reading

I had read an article about vision training and the statement had stuck in my mind "Do you see what I mean". Children struggle with vision problems in that they can see the words but they can't see what they mean.

Reading and writing were the two main tasks that were the problem.

When you read, you need to aim both eyes at the same place and accurately, focus both eyes to make the reading material clear and then keep your focus to move both eyes continually across the line of print.

When we move our eyes to the next line of print we do the same process again.

To build up comprehension when reading we are constantly taking in visual information and decoding it from written word into a mental image.

I could especially see the difficulty that dyslexic children have in that in using words that have no image i.e. it, is, let; this makes the process so difficult.

Memory and visualization are also used to constantly relate the information to what is known and to help make sense of what is being read.

Writing

When you write it is the reverse of reading in that we start with the image in our mind of the word and decode it into words.

Because of a lack of writing skills you usually find that children will invariably have a weakness in their fine motor skills because of this.

Children will then control the movement of the pencil and at the same time try to make the word make sense. While attempting to do this they will also focus their eyes and move them together, the same as the reading process.

I could at last understand why the child who had difficulty reading and writing and the child who was diagnosed with peripheral problems (fields) was unable to progress.

Auditory (Ears)

When you look up Auditory Dyslexia it can also be known as "dysphonic" dyslexia. Whatever they call it, you still need to know how to deal with it.

Auditory dyslexia is when you are not able to link or retain the auditory equivalent of a word/letter to the visual image. This creates problems in learning to read because a child will have phonological processing problems in attaching speech sounds to letters and letter combinations. If a beginning reader cannot attach sounds to letters, they cannot use sounding out procedures to identify words and this slows down reading skills.

CAPD (Central Auditory Processing Difficulty)

This is a term used to describe what happens when your brain recognizes and interprets the sounds around you.

Central auditory processing is basically the role the brain plays in the hearing process, which enables us to develop learning skills.

It is our brain and not our ears that hear. The ears play a big part in sending information on for further analysis where it is deciphered by the hearing centres of the brain. How the information is interpreted by the brain depends on our level of central auditory skills developed during the periods of language learning at the ages of 0-3 years. This is when the brain is most prepared to map information from sounds or spoken words.

CAPD, APD, auditory perception, auditory comprehension deficit, central auditory dysfunction, central deafness, and so called "word deafness" are just some of the labels used to describe auditory difficulties.

When you read the list of difficulties that are related to CAPD, they all relate to many of the similarities of children with dyspraxia:

» attention

» remembering information

» multiple directions/instructions

» poor listening

» more time to process

» behaviour problems

» reading

» comprehension

» spelling

Again, research shows that the cause of APD is unknown but in children it could be associated with conditions such as dyslexia, attention deficit disorder (ADD) autism, autism spectrum disorder, specific language impairment, developmental disorder. Sometimes this term has been misapplied to children who have no hearing or language disorder but have challenges in learning.

Again, as in visual difficulties, the same behaviours the same diagnosis.

Speech & Language / Oral Kinesthetic (Mouth)

This is the most complex area I have ever dealt with. I thought when I started working with children many years ago that, stupidly, if a child had difficulty speaking (expressive), that was the problem.

I had myself encountered a speech therapist as the youngest of my three children had shown signs of difficulties in this area.

My child (of 3 years old) was assessed and I was assured, following sleepless nights of worrying, that my health visitor (a new and inexperienced young girl) had mistook my child's lack of speech to be a natural occurrence in a family who pampered to her every whim. She was given everything she needed without having to lift a finger or the necessity to need to speak.

"How old are you?"

"She's three."

"What is your dolly called?"

"It's called Molly," we would all chorus.

It wasn't until I assessed a child in Year 6 that I realised, through ignorance, as always there was a bigger problem.

I already knew there was a gap in screening children for motor skills with the amount of children who had been on the programme. I was also aware that children on the programme with verbal dyspraxia had never been screened for dyspraxia, although it had been mentioned along the line that they all had slight difficulties in their motor skills. Once again, if these children had not attended a school which offered screening and an exercise programme, these children would never have overcome or reached their full potential.

I was asked to assess a child in Year 6 who was almost 10 and read at any opportunity, he was "a bookworm" and loved to sit quietly in a corner and read. He didn't have many friends because I thought, as most people did, that he was a "studious" little chap. He had a problem writing and found great difficulty in building up a story and his spelling was terrible.

This child never made one mistake reading very difficult text but when it came to asking him about the book (the comprehension) or his understanding (receptive) he couldn't recall a thing.

I started noticing younger children picking up free reader books and they would read back to you with ease but, ask them questions about the story, and they struggled. Children work it out that if you go up in stages and eventually become a free reader, you are seen by your peers as being really clever. They would come across difficult words and be able to decode them or memorise high frequency words. They stored up their word bank but hadn't got a clue what "divulged" and "optimistic" really meant.

Children should be comfortable with books and enjoy the whole process of reading. It can be a time they can share with parents and friends. They should also be challenged and have a choice but learning to read is an important skill.

This is not every child, but you can see if you don't consistently assess children you just take this area for granted that they are alright.

I always remember a conversation I had with a colleague who had moved back to England after living in Greece for almost 20 years. She had moved to Greece unable to speak a word of their language. I was saying how difficult it was teaching reading and writing to a child with speech and language difficulties. She said, "You learn to speak a foreign language before you read and write."

In school you encourage (usually as a rule) children to be quiet when a teacher talks to the class. Children are encouraged to use partner voices in class and very rarely are encouraged to "have a chat and a gossip." They have to focus and work, that's what they are there for, to listen and learn.

As with Jack, playtime was the most daunting of times when he would fall and not be able to process information quickly enough to "join in".

"Joining in" means you learn the basic skills of communication that are required to keep up in school and in life.

Children who have SLD in Nursery are usually delayed and need a few years to experience using speech. They still get an opportunity in Reception to verbally interact but as soon as they go into Year 1 they are on the treadmill of education, at a speed of the National Curriculum.

Speech and language are extremely complex and a lot of things can go wrong with their development. Some children are described as having a "delayed language problem" which means that their language is developing slower than in most children of their age.

In most Nurseries children are constantly being monitored and assessed to enable them to achieve the expected stages. Some children, however, have a speech, language and communication disorder which means that one or more aspects of their language development fails to develop.

Some children may have difficulty articulating some or all of the sounds that go to make up speech (d, g, s, w,) or putting them together to make whole words. I have worked with a child who only used what seemed to be vowel sounds and would say, for example, "i ~ o-u-ee" which meant "sit over here". After a while, as most mothers do, I understood him completely as I became tuned into his speech.

Children with language problems may have difficulty understanding language (receptive language) or producing words and putting them together to make coherent sentences (expressive language).

Many children can have delayed speech due to a hearing difficulty, such as glue ear, so hearing must be checked.

For some children there is a specific language disorder/difficulty. Although the child's language is delayed, their general intelligence and ability may be average or even high for their age. For these children, their understanding (receptive) is usually affected as well as their use (expressive).

Research has shown that children with expressive language disorders were rated as more socially withdrawn and anxious.

Imagine a child who has verbal dyspraxia/dyspraxia and they have delayed processing because of weakened neural pathways and delayed speech. Again, with the programme, their pathways were strengthened and speed of processing increased.

If a child also had dyspraxia, the delayed processing is bound to influence social interaction as well as their speech. But without intervention a child with these difficulties would surely struggle for years.

Research has shown the association between language difficulties and antisocial behaviour increases with age. As with many children with special needs, behaviour is sometimes used as an avoidance strategy.

Often children with specific language difficulties also have difficulties in understanding social situations, in seeing the other point of view, in using their imagination and in handling conversations. Sometimes these children are described as having pragmatic difficulties.

The child I described previously in the book with significant motor skills difficulties, and was thought to have autistic behaviours, had difficulty with processing language quickly and reacted badly to situations.

Once this child had been on the programme his processing increased and he was able to deal with situations and became less frustrated.

Although he was later diagnosed to have pragmatic difficulties, these were less prominent once the other weaknesses had been dealt with.

11. Catch Up

I saw an article recently, highlighting Dyspraxia Centres for children and adults. One of the main disadvantages was the cost of the initial screening and then the continued cost for assessment. I visited one of these centres and was amazed at the technology on offer. A child was screened and analysed using the highest quality machines and then re-assessed and monitored over a period of up to three years in some cases. I was very impressed but was shocked at the price of the whole package. If you are a parent who can afford it, that is fine. However, the majority of special needs children who may be at School Action Plus or with a Statement are not given the funding of a few thousand pounds to spend on these centres, but for many parents, who are desperate and vulnerable because they will do anything for their child, this is a light at the end of the tunnel. For most parents, if a child needs anything, "whatever the cost" they will find it.

Research quoted in the article disputed the effectiveness of such centres and children's progress educationally following attendance.

I personally think exercise is beneficial to all children and through experience, and very hard work, know that children with motor skills difficulties need specific exercises.

The reason the children in our school are so successful is because we looked at the whole picture. These special centres may deal with motor skills difficulties but we took the children back to basics in their education.

If you had two years off from walking you wouldn't expect to just walk again, you would need to learn the basic skills and build up the muscles, and that is what we did with our children.

Nursery

Imagine a child who has just started school, already a year or two behind in their development. Maybe their speech and language, motor skills, hearing and visual (the four modalities) are delayed by almost two years. They may only have one year in Nursery and some children may never have accessed a Nursery setting before. For these children, just social interaction with other children is a new experience. When assessed they are reaching targets no higher than a three year old.

Assessment in Nursery
3-4 years old ~ (Clumsy, poor concentration, high motor activity or limited movement, not following instructions, poor toileting, and minimal social interaction with peers and adults).

Reception

Children are expected to conform to the routine of a classroom. They are expected to follow rules and learn. They may have one or all of the above difficulties and are expected, when assessed, to progress with targets like all the other children in the class. Through continued assessment the class teacher will notice that a child is not achieving the set targets but puts it down to immaturity. The class teacher (if you are unlucky) may be a newly qualified teacher or may not have the experience and knowledge to notice a problem. Many people will disagree but I have seen and heard many teachers and support staff who know very little about special needs children. I know because I was one of them, years ago.

This year, I now realise, is the most important in school life as this is where any child's difficulties should be picked up, monitored and dealt with. In our Reception year this is where we start with the "Letters and Sounds" programme. At this stage a child needs to learn the sounds of the alphabet, blending, rhyming and segmenting. Most Nurseries will have given opportunities throughout the day for children to access and explore letters and numbers.

Children need phonemic awareness at this early stage, but phonemic awareness is not phonics, it is auditory and does not involve words in print.

The ability to hear and manipulate the sounds in a spoken word and syllables are made up of sequences of speech sounds (Yopp, 1992 ;)

It is essential for children learning to read in an alphabetic writing system and letters represent sounds or phonemes. Without phonemic awareness phonics mean little sense.

Imagine a child blending sounds to make a word and connecting sounds with their written symbols.

Blending   Cccccccccccc aaaaaaa tttttt

Segmenting is the ability to recognise the initial sound Cat

Segmenting is the ability to recognise the final sound cat

Segmenting is the ability to recognise (complete) sounds in a word CAT

Sound and Word Discrimination

» Can tell whether words or sounds are the same or different (cat/cat or cat/can)

» Can tell which word is different (hen, pen, hen)

» Can tell the difference between single speech sounds (e, e, p)

Rhyming

» Can identify whether words rhyme (cat, mat /ring, sing)

» Can produce a word that rhymes (rose, nose) and can continue with the pattern.

Blending

» Blends 2-3 separately spoken phonemes into one syllable words (i-t: it; c-a-t: cat;)

» Can orally blend syllables (car-pet) or onset –rimes(m-ilk)

Segmentation

» Claps or counts the words in a 3-5 word sentence (I…will…sit…down)

» Claps or counts the syllables in 2- and 3 syllable words

» Identifies the first sound in a one syllable word (/c/ … cat)

» Segments individual sounds in 2 and 3 phoneme, one-syllable words (fat … f/a/t)

"The best predictor of reading difficulty in kindergarten or first grade is the inability to segment words and syllables into constituent sound units (phonemic awareness)." (Lyon, 1995)

Assessment in Reception

4–5 years old ~ (Clumsy, poor concentration, high motor activity or limited movement, not following instructions, poor toileting, unsettled in school, truancy, continued attempted avoidance of PE, emotional, limited interaction.)

Year 1 ~ School Action

5–6 years old ~ (Clumsy, poor concentration, high motor activity or limited movement, not following instructions, poor toileting, eating problems, social problems, unsettled in school, truancy, avoidance of PE, difficulty progressing in literacy and numeracy.)

At this point the school recognises that the child has a problem and is put on the Special Needs Register.

Year 2

6–7 years old ~ (Clumsy, poor concentration, high motor activity or limited movement, not following instructions, poor toileting, eating problems, social problems, unsettled in school, truancy, avoidance of PE, difficulty in accessing the National Curriculum as assessed to be almost two years behind their cognitive age.)

Discussions with parents (three weeks) health visitor, hearing tests, eyes tested, social worker, speech and language. All the information is collated and reports sent to the school which could take months.

A meeting with the child's parents, SENCO, class teacher and support assistant is arranged.

The advice is to move the child up to up to School Action Plus and be assessed by an Educational Psychologist. An Individual Educational Plan is drawn up to aim for small targets the child can achieve. The child will be put into a small group with support but will have no funding for this as it will be general support. Again a meeting is arranged with all the relevant agencies but this depends on whether staff required are ill, on holiday, or are fully booked for months because they are the only ones available in 21 schools in your area. They could send a report but have no administration at the moment.

Year 3

7–8 years old ~ (Clumsy, poor concentration, high motor activity or limited movement, not following instructions, poor toileting, eating problems, social problems, unsettled in school, truancy, avoidance of PE, difficulty in accessing the National Curriculum as assessed to be almost three years behind their cognitive age.)

Discussion with parents and outside agency, advice from Speech and Language, health visitor, general practitioner, Occupational Therapists, Educational Psychologist, Portex and "The Butterfly Project" (to support the parents and child at home and school).

To apply for New Approaches funding for extra support.

And so it goes on as the child rises up the SEN register. The school will do as much as possible to support this child but this all depends on funding and resources of staff. One other factor is how many other children in the same class have needs that require support.

A child without difficulties progresses at the required pace every parent and teacher hopes. Children are expected to move at a steady pace in school but the National Curriculum was not developed for special needs children.

Luckily, you can eliminate many of these years of struggling, frustration and failure.

In our school, through early intervention, we have children in Reception/Year 1 on a programme. We are now working at the same time on their phonemic awareness so that the gap between themselves and their peers won't widen too dramatically.

Our screening and programme is free.

Because children have been unable to reach their potential because of MSD and some children have lost precious years, they are able to catch up with specific support in class.

We may not have high-tech equipment (hoops, beanbags, masking tape and skateboards) but it is effective and works. Children laugh at me, at themselves or just because they are happy and they are with other children who are just the same as them.

They may not have reams of printed out evidence that they can file and save (although I have a before and after writing on standard A4 paper that I am very proud of ~ WOW!).

They will be given a certificate in the hall (not to humiliate them) as well as showing their work off in class. They can burst with pride at applause from the whole class at their achievements even if it is just being able to catch a ball in PE.

As a parent I struggled and worried that I had to find extra money to pay for the basic milk money, dinners, trips, photos, parties, presents and the list goes on.

I have been there when parents have been informed that their child is having difficulties and witnessed the emotion and despair.

Weeks, months and years after children have progressed and the emotion has changed to happiness without the financial burden.

Simple, effective and free!

Motor Skills Program

Name...

Date........................ Week............................

Activity	Mon	Tues	Wed	Thur	Fri
Feet together, jump along 2 measured lines, 5 times. *(Lower body strength, direction, balance)*					
Hop on the left/right leg, 5 times. *(Lower body strength, balance, direction, left/right laterality)*	Left Right				
Walk along a white measured line. *(Balance, direction distance, left/right)*					
Turning a skipping rope 360° each hand 20 times. Hand/arm strength, direction.	Left Right				
Throw a beanbag at a target, feet, together, face forward. Direction, balance, distance,					
Hop through 6 hoops at a slow timed pace, in, out, in, out. Direction, distance, pace.					
Throw beanbags from left to right hands, watching the beanbag. Tracking ,balance, direction.					
Sitting long sit on a skateboard pull along a rope with hands up. Direction, balance, hand strength.					
Lie face down on a skateboard walk with hands along the floor. Upper body/hand strength, direction, balance.					

Motor Skills Screening

Name.. Date............ Age......

Please take off shoes and socks before beginning...

Activity	Behaviour
1. Walking on tiptoes forwards and backwards	Look for hands down /
2. Walking on heels forwards and backwards	Look for hands up / tongue out
3. Walking on the insides of feet forwards and backwards	Hands turned out / tongue out
4. Walking on outsides of feet forwards and backwards	Hands turned in / tongue out
5. Recognising 2 fingers touched at the same time when hidden from view Right then left	Unable to recognise which fingers Slow to process the information
6. Finger sequencing / right then left	Look for mirroring on the other hand
7. Wrist rotation	Elbows out
8. Balancing on each foot	10 seconds over 4 years old
9. Eyes closed / arms extended / touching the end of the nose Right then left	Child will watch extended arm moving in or miss
10. Throwing a beanbag from left to right hand in an arch	Look for eyes fixating and following
11. Run in a circle around the hall	Arms flapping/bumping into obstacles
12. Drawing sample	Comments
13. Writing sample	Comments

Bibliography

Development Dyspraxia Identification and Intervention second edition, by Madeleine Portwood.

Page 80 ~ Yopp, 1992

Page 81 ~ Lyon, 1995

Jan 26th 2011

Been 'I'm not good at anything'
'teachers at Tavern all think art'

Tasks to
Improve kinesthetic sensitivity improve
hand writing

generate ideas
organise ideas
Do
Franklin Speaking Spelling Ace

Speed up programme.

Hand writing without Tears ——

Take time and Callirobics —

exit stroke on the 1st letter

* Write from the start —— approach to Handwriting programme.
  A perceptual - motor approach to Handwriting programme.
Cursive writing — making Inclusion work for children with
                              dyspraxia. — Gill dixon Book

dice throwing - no = activity

Grid paper

Triangular Pencils   Pen Pal Scheme
hand hugger Pens
Sharing Foam   Cursive upstroke
on back
diagonal lines